The Legend
of
the Green Man

The Legend of the Green Man

BY

SARA HELY

Random House   New York

Library of Congress Cataloging in Publication Data
Hely, Sara.
The legend of the green man.
I. Title.
PZ4845Le3   [PR6058. E4915]   823'.9'14   72-7479
ISBN 0-394-48385-5

Manufactured in the United States of America
by The Haddon Craftsmen, Inc.

2 4 6 8 9 7 5 3

First American Edition

For
Anna and Anne

The Legend
of
the Green Man

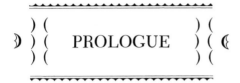

) (
)) (PROLOGUE) ((
) (

THEY SHOULD, of course, have hanged Paddy Kelagher in Clonmel. If Sir William Fossick had followed his inclination, they would undoubtedly have done so. Nor would they have wasted any time over the business. Hangings were commonplace enough in those spring days of 1799. If Sir William had succeeded in having his way (which he usually did), there would have been no trouble.

In old Lord Comeragh's opinion, however, Kelagher was in a class apart from other felons. The murderer of his grandson was to be hanged on Kilnabawn Bridge, and the world was to see Harry St. Dennis solemnly avenged. Sir William might have managed to make the old man see that this was impractical, theatrical, and unnecessary, but he did not try

(3)

to do so. He had his reasons for wishing to oblige his Lordship. So, on Sir William's orders, they put Paddy Kelagher into a high-sided cart, bound his hands behind him, put a noose about his strong young neck, and brought him outside the prison walls. They surrounded the cart with a strong military guard. Sir William was determined that nothing should go wrong.

It was all of six miles from Clonmel to Kilnabawn Bridge, and on the day of the execution it was very cold and pouring with rain. Sir William Fossick, the deputy sheriff of that part of the county, rode at the head of the procession. At his side was Captain Dillon, who was in command of the red-coated guards. Sir William had taken every possible precaution, had sent troops to guard every turning; yet he did not feel easy.

There was no doubt that Kelagher's trial had caused a tiresome amount of commotion and excitement among the uneducated and disaffected rabble. Not only among the poor, either. Several persons had said that the trial had been rushed, that the witnesses had been bribed, and so on. There was really very little danger that anyone would overpower the guards. Not even that half-fictitious hero of the poor country people, the Green Man, could achieve that, thought Sir William sourly. Still, it would take very little to set fire to the explosive tempers of the crowd, thereby turning Lord Comeragh's plan for a somber, awe-inspiring ceremony into an undignified riot.

The slow pace of the cortege was beginning to exasperate Sir William almost beyond bearing, but with the road so muddied and uneven, and the crowds pressing in on all sides, it was not possible to travel any faster. If only they reached Kilnabawn Bridge without incident, all would be well, but the way ahead was curtained in mist and rain, and it seemed to Sir William as if the journey would never end.

At every turning of the road, at every cabin door, small

groups of people were gathered. Some came running, summoned by the steady beat of the drums. The doomed man, bruised about the face and of a ragged and unkempt appearance, was nevertheless a figure of some dignity. He managed, somehow, to keep himself upright in his cruelly jolting conveyance. Some of the onlookers sank to their knees at the sight of him, and stayed kneeling in the mud of the road until the procession had gone by. These were the exceptions, however, as for every person who watched them go, there were ten to join the marchers, and before they had gone a mile, the whole road was thronged as far as the eye could see.

If it were not for the macabre nature of the expedition, it might almost have been a fair-day atmosphere which was developing. The noise and the crowd grew with every mile, and two gaily painted tinkers' caravans appeared from a side road, and were seen lurching and bowing above the sea of people like colorful galleons.

"Keep an eye on those tinkers, Captain Dillon," said Sir William. "We don't want any trouble there."

"No, indeed," replied the captain. He was just as anxious as Sir William to get the whole distasteful business over, and the deputy sheriff's fidgets were only making matters worse. "Still, they can't do any harm . . ."

"Don't be too sure, Captain. They will try anything, those tinkers . . ."

"Surely there is very little they can do, sir, even if they wanted to. I know the man Kelagher is said to be kin to the tinkers, but still . . ."

"Keep an eye on them, Dillon, that's all," said Sir William testily and drew his cloak more closely about his neck. He felt jumpy and out of sorts. He swung his whip threateningly at a small boy who was pressing too close to his horse, and told the child to be off. The child, far from cringing away, made a rude face at him and darted off through a gap in the crowd.

There was a spattering of laughter in the throng, quickly suppressed but unmistakable. Sir William did not appear to heed the laughter, any more than he heeded the sullen looks which were cast in his direction, but he looked forward all the more to the moment when they would reach the bridge. When at last they rounded the last bend in the road and saw its dark arc against the winter tracery of trees, he knew a strong sensation of relief.

Having set his heart on having his grandson's murderer hanged in the most public and salutary manner, Lord Comeragh had gone on to plan every detail. A gallows had been built at the very center of the bridge, and its ominous angles jutted high above the gray stone parapet, over the central arch which spanned the swollen and turbulent river. As a stage, the bridge could hardly have been bettered. Its humped stone shape rose high above the road, spanning the river at an angle.

As they came nearer, Sir William could see that the hangman was ready and waiting beneath the gallows. It had been Lord Comeragh who had insisted on this nice macabre touch, and Sir William had arranged it all. So long as Kelagher was strung up, he did not greatly care how it was done, and with a solid phalanx of infantry drawn up at each entrance to the bridge, he began to feel wholly confident again. There could be no escape for Paddy Kelagher now; not unless he chose to hurl himself into the river, and with the waters in flood, swollen and surging through the bridge, it could only be another way for him to die. And come to that, thought Sir William, the hangman was unlikely to let his prey escape him. The Clonmel hangman was a brutally efficient practitioner of his grisly trade. He was waiting for them, decked out in a plum-colored coat, masked as was his habit, and wearing a curly-brimmed beaver hat.

This he doffed as Sir William rode up, with the prisoner's

cart rumbling behind him. "Well, sir," he cried in his fruity voice, " 'tis a grand crowd you've got today, and that's a fact. And all for only the one hanging! Have you no more, sir?" Sir William smiled grimly, his fair, strong, rain-wet face glistening beneath the brim of his hat. "No. Only the one for you today, Mick, as you very well know. And once Father Murphy has finished, make as quick a job of it as you're able. I'll make it worth your while."

"Don't you fret, Sir William," cried the hangman, so loudly that Sir William could gladly have throttled him with his own rope. "I'll not keep you long from your dinner. I'll have that divil strung up before you can turn your head. But is the old lord not coming? 'Tis a wonder he's not been here this half hour or more . . ."

"Lord Comeragh is indisposed," replied Sir William repressively.

He glanced to where the priest had clambered up beside the prisoner in his cart. The truth was that Lord Comeragh had just sent word to say that he was in the gout again. Doubtless the exertions of planning the execution and his usual immoderate intake of port wine had proved too much for the earl's seventy-year-old constitution.

"No, he'll not be coming," Sir William went on, "but you may be sure I shall give him a faithful account of it all . . ."

The hangman said loudly, shouting above the roar of the flood water and the cries and clatter of the crowd assembled at each end of the bridge, "They tell me, sir, that his Lordship's taken a mighty fancy to you these days . . ."

"Now, see here," said Sir William firmly, "your task is to hang Kelagher. Mine is to see it done. Let us have less talk, if you please."

"Whatever you say, sir," replied the hangman, in no way abashed. "As soon as his Reverence is done, I'll have the boy

(7)

dancing on the rope . . ." He glanced sideways at the deputy sheriff. "Would you do something for me, sir?"

"I might. What is it?"

"Would you take this for me, sir?" He held out a bulging leather purse. " 'Twould be a disaster entirely if it slipped from me while I was over the water . . ."

"Oh, give it to the corporal," said the deputy sheriff impatiently. "I've no fancy to play at lady's maid."

It was only a matter of minutes before Father Murphy climbed down from the prisoner's cart. He stood, bareheaded and rotund in his robes, as the horses were whipped forward and the doomed man was maneuvered to his appointed place beneath the gallows.

The drums, which had been tap-tapping grimly all the while at the south entrance to the bridge, now changed their rhythm to a slow, thunderous roll. Captain Dillon gave a signal to the bugler, and a blast was blown.

Above the roar of the water below him, Sir William could hardly hear the tumult of the crowd. Was it imagination, then, or did the bugle's harsh notes herald a hush among the multitudes who pressed up behind the massed soldiers? He saw a ragged boy wave a red handkerchief.

Sir William then turned to the prisoner and asked him if he had anything to say. The fellow turned his head and eyed Sir William in a bewildered, despairing way; but he said nothing. All the time Paddy had been in prison, he had gazed at his interrogators with that hangdog look, and if Sir William expected any last-minute change, he was disappointed.

He waited a moment longer, then raised his right hand and nodded to the hangman. The ropes which bound Kelagher to the cart were cut, the noose was fastened more securely round his neck, and the free end of the rope was flung up to the soldier who was waiting aloft to catch it. The prisoner's lips seemed to move.

The hangman gave vent to a hoarse chuckle and said, "Right you be, Sir William! Turn your head away and count to five, and I'll have this lad in the air for you."

Sir William allowed his grim face to relax into the merest flicker of a smile. "I'm not so frail a fellow that I cannot watch you at work, Mick."

"You're a marvel, sir! A man after me heart . . ." The soldier came down from his perch, climbing down the wooden ladder and landing with a hollow clatter on the scaffold boarding. He handed the rope end to the hangman and went to join the other militiamen, who were some distance away. The hangman nodded to the prisoner. Sir William stiffened.

Kelagher stepped forward meekly, and at a word from the hangman he began his painstaking and awkward ascent. His hands were still tied behind him, so the hangman went up the ladder at his back, steadying him and holding tightly to the rope end. Then, when he judged the prisoner to be high enough, he stepped onto the parapet of the bridge and the prisoner was left alone on the ladder.

Momentarily both hangman and felon were pinned, motionless, against the sullen sky. Then the hangman moved again. He moved so swiftly, in fact, that it was some seconds before Sir William realized what had happened. He sat there on his horse, gazing spellbound at where, one moment before, the hangman and the prisoner had been. The stone parapet was bare and empty. Both of them were gone.

A moment later he came to his senses and plunged forward to the side of the bridge. He was too late. Too late, that was, to save the disastrous situation. He was in time, however, to see the flat, bobbing craft tearing away upon the surging current of the river, and on it he could just distinguish the prone form of Paddy Kelagher and the crouching, protective figure of the hangman in his plum-colored coat.

(9)

AS WAS TO BE EXPECTED, they said it was the Green Man and not the hangman at all. There had been whispers about the Green Man all winter long, for the atmosphere of terror and bewilderment which prevailed in the months after the 1798 uprising had proved to be a perfect breeding ground for extravagant tales and myths of this kind.

The name of the Green Man had become a talisman of hope for the poor country people, a name to be remembered when the soldiers were out in the night, beating their peremptory tattoos upon cabin doors, seeking for hidden arms, setting fire to thatch. The country people had need of a ray of hope in those days, and hope was all that remained for some: hope—and an enduring delight in the ridiculous.

The hangman's purse had been a source of joy. Everyone knew that the Green Man was in the habit of leaving ivy leaves in place of a calling card. The hangman's purse was found to be full of ivy leaves weighted by pebbles, and Sir William Fossick's discomfiture had been too evident to be hidden. For more than anything, the Green Man was loved because he managed to make a laughingstock of the authorities, and with the Paddy Kelagher affair he had done it again. Into the dark days of that time, the Green Man had brought another blessed leavening of laughter.

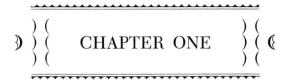

CHAPTER ONE

THE UNWIELDY CARRIAGE drew up with a lurch, waking Kitty Harcombe from her stiff, frozen doze. She leaned forward and fumbled with the leather blind at the carriage window, and even as she did so the door was wrenched open from the outside.

"Well, ma'am," said the coachman, peering at his passengers by the light of a grimy lantern, "is it dead ye all are in there?"

Kitty put a hand to her exceedingly fashionable bonnet and peered past him into the darkness. Dimly she could see the outline of a door. It was very large and looked to be studded with iron nails. It was also very firmly closed.

"What is this place?" she demanded in her cool, slightly

drawling voice. "Why have you stopped? I made it plain to you that Sir William Fossick would pay you handsomely if you would bring us safe to Mount Comeragh this evening."

" 'Tis safe enough ye are, ma'am," replied the coachman, snorting disrespectfully. Plainly there was no pleasing the grand London lady. He raised his lantern higher so that its beams licked over the sleeping face of Kitty's five-year-old son, revealing also the large figure of Martha, Kitty's maid. In a more indulgent tone, the coachman demanded whether he should knock at the door.

"Of course. At once!"

Kitty had been tired and cold for so long that she had not thought it possible to feel any worse. But she found herself mistaken. In all the vicissitudes and discomforts of their precipitate journey she had refused to be daunted. Martha's complaints, little Robert's bouts of sickness, the insolence of inn servants who saw no need to exert themselves for a lady traveling without proper escort—all these things she had been able to bear with inward equanimity. The landlord at Milford Haven had certainly been given no inkling of that inward calm of hers when he had been unable to provide her with a private parlor, nor had the blacksmith at Cheltenham when he had been slow to do her bidding. But it had been so. Even when Sir William's carriage had not been at Waterford to meet them, she had been no more than momentarily dismayed. After all, it would be almost worth the jolting they had been given in the shabby old hired carriage to see William's face when they arrived upon his doorstep. How she would roast him for failing to meet her! William was always so careful of the proprieties. He had been forever in danger of being shocked by her less strait-laced acquaintances. He would now be shocked beyond measure.

But it seemed that the pleasure of startling William was to be deferred yet again. Kitty had been buoyed up for so long by the thought of their arrival at Mount Comeragh, and during the last cold hours of their journey had imagined it to be such a positive haven of warmth and hospitality, that the sight of that closed door caused her to feel utterly downcast. No lights glimmered anywhere. She felt the last of her precarious courage draining away.

Sharply she said, "Are you sure this is Mount Comeragh?"

But the man had already turned away with a surly swagger. He began to hammer upon the door, banging a heavy wrought-iron knocker with vigor. The hammering seemed to go on and on. A gusty winter wind tore at the open door of the carriage, and little Robert began to stir and to cough again in that dry distressful way.

Martha sniffed balefully in the gloom. "Close the carriage door, milady, for goodness' sake. Didn't I tell you over and over again that we ought not to have set out from Waterford in this mad-brained way. No, nor ought we to have come into Ireland at all! A dirty, heathen country from all I can see."

Robert began to cry wearily. "There! There!" said Martha fiercely and protectively. "Martha's here, love!"

The child's only reply to this endearment was to begin to cough again, and then to be suddenly sick into Martha's capacious lap.

Ignoring her maid's declaration that she would rather spend the night in a ditch than travel another yard in this outlandish conveyance, Kitty descended from the carriage and picked her way over the wet gravel to where the coachman was still creating enough din to waken the countryside for miles around.

She waited for him to pause. "It seems that my message has gone astray," she said at last, with a calm born of despair. "Though I cannot at all understand why all the servants should be absent, even if their master is away. We will have to put up at a local inn until morning."

(13)

"Local inn, is it?" The coachman rolled a derisive eye in Kitty's direction. "And will ye tell me where that will be, ma'am?"

It was gradually borne upon Kitty's reluctant understanding that there was no inn within miles. To reach the nearest one, indeed the nearest dwelling of any kind, they would have to go back five miles along the road and across the river.

Moreover, as the coachman informed her with gloomy relish, he had no intention of taking his horses any farther this night. There'd be straw and hay in the stables, no doubt, even if there was not a living soul to answer to his knocking. Straw and hay were good enough for his horses, and a bed in the stables good enough for him. If the grand London lady thought differently, she was welcome to take herself to some better place. He was going no farther.

Kitty gave the coachman her opinion of both his manners and his abilities as a driver, but though this relieved her feelings a little, it made it no better when she was forced to follow him as he led his equipage up the sweep of weedy gravel to the stable yard. There was nothing for it but to do so, for he had the advantage of possessing the only two lanterns, one in his hand and the other hitched to the front of the carriage. From anything she could see in the gloom, mere fleeting glimpses lit by the passing lantern glow, the house was of a sprawling vastness.

She had not expected William's residence to be anything like so large. He had given her no inkling of this decayed grandeur, of row upon row of blank windows shuttered from within and showing no chink of light. From the brief impression that Kitty was afforded as they went along, she thought that William had been neglecting the upkeep of his establishment of late. This supposition was borne out by the rutted condition of the roadway they were following and by a trail of wet ivy which overhung the arched entrance to the stables. There was no light in the stables, either, but to Kitty's grateful ear there came the soft snorting of a horse. Her reason told her that where there were horses, there would eventually be people. The coachman seemed to think the same, and went off to investigate.

To Kitty the thought of a straw bed in the loft seemed suddenly unbearably sweet. She could have slept anywhere at that moment, so long as it was dry and warm. She was reminded, however, by the muttering from within the carriage that Martha would be very much harder to please. For all her talk of wishing to sleep in a ditch, Kitty could picture all too vividly how her portly maid would receive the suggestion that the hayloft was to be their bed. Martha's standards of behavior and propriety were as firmly fixed as the steel supports of her corsets. Scenes with Martha were always tedious and Kitty was in no humor for one, so with some idea of postponing it, she unhooked the remaining lantern from the carriage and set off to try to gain entrance to the house.

The back regions of the place were a labyrinth of archways, windows, doors with peeling paint and unrelenting latches. The rain grew heavier, and streams of water eddied everywhere, swirling down gutters, cascading from overhanging eaves and broken pipes. Kitty's hat was soon nothing but a sodden wreck, and her French leather gloves had grown so slippery that it was difficult to grip a door handle firmly enough to turn it. A seeping trickle of coldness was feeling its way down her spine, and presently she decided that the hayloft would have to do. There was nothing to be gained from staying out in the rain, trying doors and windows that were firmly barred, and hammering upon them to waken servants who, to all appearances, must be dead or gone. She was retracing her steps, which was not easy in the bewildering maze of buildings, when she caught sight of another door. She paused, and then tried it. It yielded to a push and she almost fell into the house.

She drew a breath of relief. Robert must be brought in from the rain without delay, for he was unwell. First, though, she must find a bed to put him in. She took off her limp hat and her gloves and threw them down. Then, her lantern held high, she began to walk down the corridor, looking into one after another of the rooms which led off it.

Her growing astonishment at the shabbiness of the house changed into something more like alarm. This was no temporarily deserted home; it looked as if it had not been lived in, or tended, for years. It was filthy and smelled of mold, and she was forced to wonder if William and his sister had ever lived in this decaying ruin, and if so, what manner of persons they could be.

Had they been deliberately trying to deceive her as to their circumstances? Was William's air of fastidiousness, his elegant clothes, his appearance of authority and affluence as much a mockery and a sham as the idea he had conveyed to her of his house? In all the dozens of letters she had received from him he had painstakingly described his neighbors, his lands, the improvements he was making to the house and to the garden, hoping, as he said, to provoke her into coming to see them for herself. (How he longed to see his dearest Kitty in his new book-room at Mount Comeragh!) He had expressed himself pleased with this room, and had covered fully three pages with his neat writing in his efforts to convey to her some idea of its magnificence: the walls lined with leather-bound books, the woodwork gilded and carved, and the fine plaster work on the ceiling which he had designed himself.

And what of Miss Fossick's effusive and all but illegible scrawls which had enumerated the delights of the assemblies they attended in nearby Clonmel? Miss Fossick had enthused about card parties and the other social delights of the Tipperary scene in which dear William was quite one of the leading lights.

Only a few weeks back Kitty and her fashionable friends had been in fits over their efforts to untangle Miss Fossick's latest innocent and countrified epistle. Now that the Rebellion had been quelled, it read, all was gaiety and dissipation.

Kitty remembered how Wandlebury had nipped the letter from her hand and had insisted on reading it aloud to the company. And Kitty, though protesting, had been as convulsed with laughter as any of them.

She had no thought, then, of accepting William's invitation to visit him at Mount Comeragh. She admitted to a certain fondness for him, it was true, but she had no intention of trailing all the way to his outlandish country in the midst of the London season. She had made it clear that if he wished to see more of her, to woo her, he must leave his tiresome duties and his even more tiresome Ireland with its horrid disturbances and threatened invasions and come to London to see her.

Now things were different. Thinking back upon her precipitate, panic-driven departure from London, Kitty was unable to deny that she had behaved like a coward. Her courage, and she had once thought she possessed a good deal of it, had been completely overthrown by the sudden tumult of scandal and disapproval which had risen up around her.

It all happened so suddenly that there had been no time to arm herself; and with Lady Wandlebury behaving in such an underbred way, she found herself cold-shouldered by people whom she had safely judged to be her friends. The Harcombes were angry with her, her own brother expressed himself disgusted, and after that last assembly at Almack's she had vowed that she would tolerate no more of it. She would go to Ireland, and when she returned they would all have some new scandal to occupy their minds.

Accordingly, Kitty had sent a letter to William, and the next day she had bundled Martha and Robert into her traveling chaise, taking with her enough boxes and trunks to be sure of putting Miss Fossick and her dissipated neighbors into a dazzle, and had set out on the road to Milford Haven without telling anyone where she was going. She hoped that her brother and her Harcombe relations would be worried at her sudden disappearance. After the way they had lectured her about her flirtation with Wandlebury—as though she were to blame if he found her more diverting than his silly little wife—Kitty had been quite out of charity with all of them.

The journey had been remarkably unpleasant. A broken axle near Cheltenham had been the first of a series of mishaps. It had been impossible to hire another chaise without waiting a whole day for it, and Kitty, in one of those spurts of impetuosity for which she was notorious, had decided to abandon her coachman and to travel on by stagecoach. She had not, of course, been prepared to abandon her trunks of dresses, her hatboxes, and any of the other necessary paraphernalia of her existence, and there had been a deal of trouble with the driver of the stage over these. However, she had prevailed upon him to take them (some other unfortunate persons had it explained to them that there would not, after all, be room for them on the coach that day), but though she triumphed in this, she came near to regretting it several times.

Martha scolded all the way, and little Robert's cough grew worse each day. She was only prevented from turning back by her own natural stubbornness and the thought of giving William such a charming surprise. Whoever else might carp or disapprove, William was sure to be delighted with her. It had been a constant consolation, with all the world against her, to dwell in her thoughts upon the promise of William's uncritical admiration. To this certainty she had clung throughout the whole uncomfortable journey from London to County Tipperary.

Now she was no longer sure of anything. It was ten o'clock of a cold March evening, and she was growing ever more certain, as she picked her way past a door which hung crazily upon one hinge, that this could not possibly be William's house. Certainly, when he had offered for her hand formally, on his knees, he had assured her earnestly that he could not aspire to give her many of the luxuries to which she was accustomed, but she had never seen anything like this monstrous mansion. Holding up her lantern again, she gazed about her with fascinated horror.

She was at one end of a huge hall. The ceiling was vastly high and the walls had once been paneled in some somber wood. Something of the magnificence of the place still clung to it, but the hands which had ripped the wooden paneling from the walls and flung two gigantic carved chandeliers onto the marble floor had done their best to leave no single piece of furniture in a whole or usable condition. Pictures had been hacked from their frames, curtains slashed. Everywhere there were sad heaps of cobweb-strewn debris: the corpses of chairs, a shattered china ornament, a charred rag of silk. At the far end of the hall, dimly visible, was a staircase. It led upward into a cavern of darkness, and for all Kitty's vaunted resolution, she could not bring herself to step across the hall and march up the stairs. Probably there was nothing more terrible in that brooding darkness than empty rooms and more cobwebs, but she did not intend to find out.

She stood where she was, listening intently for any sign of life, yet fearing to hear any. Then something scuffled in the darkness of the hall. It was a soft sound, probably a bat or a bird, but it was enough to send Kitty scurrying out of the hall, and in a moment she was fleeing back down the passage. Martha would have to make do with the stables.

One of the doors of the corridor was ajar, so Kitty turned and looked inside. To her surprise it contained a bed, albeit a narrow one with what looked to be a straw-filled mattress, but it would do for Robert, and the room felt less damp than the great hall. It would do for the rest of the night, she thought, and in the morning she would wrestle further with the coachman and endeavor to find her way to her proper destination.

She turned to go, but got no farther than a step. In the doorway stood a large, cloaked figure, and in this man's hand there was a pistol. He was pointing it straight at her.

CHAPTER TWO

FOR A MOMENT Kitty neither moved nor spoke. She could not. Then, when the creature in the doorway still remained where he was, she drew a rapid, shallow breath and forced herself to ask, "What do you want?"

For answer he continued to hold the pistol pointing at her heart. She could not see his face, which was in shadow, and she did not dare to hold up her lantern or to move in any way lest he be startled into firing his weapon. She tried to recruit her courage by pretending to be angry.

"Are you trying to alarm me by standing there in that foolish way? If you think to rob me, I have nothing of value . . ."

"I don't want your purse. I think you know very well what I want."

His voice was deep, and quite illogically she felt reassured by it, though she could not have told herself why. She said, "I have no idea what you want, sir, but pray tell me what it is, so that I can give it to you and you may go away . . ."

"On the contrary. It is you who must go away, ma'am," and with these words he inclined his head and came through the doorway. She thought, irrelevantly, that he must be even taller than Wandlebury; and as she braced herself, forcing herself to keep still, he put the pistol away in his pocket. He took the lantern from her wavering grasp, then held it up and studied her.

She stared back at him, uneasily conscious that she was looking bedraggled and far from dignified. When she had suffered his scrutiny for a few moments, she said coldly, "Well? Are you satisfied, sir?"

He nodded, almost absently, and said, "You are not what I expected."

"I am indeed sorry if you are disappointed, sir," she said ironically, her drawl more marked than usual, "but then, I did not expect you at all."

He smiled at her: a horrid gleaming smile which lit his dark, grim countenance. "You thought to stay here un-detected, did you? Well, if you wished to do that, you should not write letters to my brother." He frowned down at her as though something about her puzzled him. "I intercepted the letter, you see."

"Your . . . brother?" echoed Kitty. She had always imag-ined that Miss Fossick was William's only relative. She shook her head in a bewildered way. "I do not seem to be able to . . . think . . . properly. I did not expect . . ."

"You did not expect me?" he supplied for her contemptu-ously. "Well, I admit that I am not in the habit of reading my brother's correspondence, but it came to my hand by mistake. I am Denny, you see."

Kitty stole a glance at his swarthy, inimical face, thought of the pistol which he had aimed so coolly at her, and felt very much afraid. There would be time enough to sort out this madman's relationship with William when she was safely out of his reach. For the present it seemed only prudent to humor him, to try to persuade him to let her go. She managed to smile up at him with a passable amount of conviction and said, "I am delighted to meet you, sir."

"Are you hoping to seduce me, ma'am?" he inquired softly. "You would stand a better chance with my more susceptible brother. You see," he added, looking her over with a cold insolence which made her flesh creep, "you see, I require rather more than a pretty smile and a beseeching air to win me round. Go back to wherever you came from, my girl, and be grateful you did not use my brother to further your schemes. If you had succeeded in that, I should have had no mercy on you . . ."

"You have misread the situation," said Kitty pleadingly, though her heart hammered violently against her ribs. Never had she seen a more threatening aspect in a man. It was as though there were banked-up fires inside him, a molten fury which was seething there, awaiting release. "I mean your brother no harm. You must try to believe that."

"Then go back to Dublin or wherever you hail from, and leave him be. If you had been Cullen, as I expected, I should have dealt more hardly with you."

"Cullen?" Kitty passed a hand wearily over her eyes, as if to dispel some of the utter bewilderment she felt.

The tall man said in a milder tone, "You are an Englishwoman, are you not?"

She nodded. Part of her mind was trying to grope with what he had said about expecting Cullen. She knew no one of that name, nor had William Fossick's letters ever mentioned him, so far as she could remember.

"Then why," he demanded with a rasping sternness which made her shrink back, "Why do you meddle with our concerns? You are not bad-looking. You appear to be gently bred. Why should you concern yourself in this game? It can only lead to disaster . . ."

Kitty said weakly, "There is some mistake. I am not what you think me . . ."

He frowned at her, puzzled, wary, and again she was almost physically conscious of the pent-up violence inside him. She said nervously, "If I had known that Miss Fossick and your brother were to be from home, I would have put up in Waterford. I journeyed so quickly, and was so anxious to press on that I never stopped to consider . . ."

"What the devil are you prattling about?" he demanded. Then in one terrifying movement he swooped forward like some great bat in his long cloak and grasped her shoulders. "Whom did you say you had come here to see?"

She said faintly, "Why, William Fossick of course."

"Good God!"

There was an odd effervescent sensation in her head and a white mist around her eyes. She closed them and swayed against him. She felt herself being lifted and laid down upon the crunching straw mattress of the bed.

When she opened her eyes, she found the tall man looking down at her in something like consternation. He met her dazed look and began hunting for something under his cloak, swearing in an undertone as he did so. He looked so perturbed, indeed, that she said with a somewhat wobbly chuckle, "Do not be concerned, sir. I shall not faint again."

He looked a good deal less forbidding when he smiled. "You relieve me, ma'am. I had hoped to find my flask in my coat pocket, but it is not there." She endeavored to sit up, feeling that she had just begun to wake up from a nightmare, but he laid a hand upon her shoulder. "No. Do not stir for a moment. I have no wish for you to turn all vaporish again."

"I am indeed sorry to have alarmed you," she murmured ironically.

"Are you?" he challenged her coolly. "I rather thought you had done it to punish me."

"No such thing," retorted Kitty crossly. "But what manner of villainess did you suppose me to be that you set upon me with such ferocity?"

He did not seem to be in any hurry to enlighten her. He sat himself down upon the only chair in the room and proceeded to remove his dark-brimmed hat and his gloves.

He was a striking-looking man, if not precisely handsome, with close-cropped black hair streaked with gray at the temples, a long-jawed, high-nosed face that looked almost swarthy in the lantern light. His eyes were dark and very bright, as though lit from within, and had a way of narrowing suddenly when he was intent or amused. Now he threw her one bright, mocking glance, as though giving her permission to study him to her heart's content, and then proceeded to help himself to snuff.

She felt that this was showing a great deal too much unconcern on his part (after all, he had only a few minutes before threatened her with violence), and she said softly, "I am still burning to know, sir, which of your acquaintances you took me for? I pity your lady friends if that is the way you treat them."

He said blandly, "They do not generally complain of my treatment of them."

"Indeed?" she retorted with polite disbelief. "You amaze me."

"And you have amazed me, too, ma'am. Did I really understand you to say that you expected to find William Fossick here?"

Kitty sat up. "Do not tell me that this is not Sir William's house? Well," she added quickly as a wicked gleam of laughter lit his dark eyes, "I did not think it, of course, but the coachman distinctly said . . ."

"How intimately," he asked her gently, "are you acquainted with Sir William Fossick?"

"What is that to the point?"

"If you knew Sir William even a little, ma'am, you would not ask that."

"A little?" Kitty's green eyes were positively flashing with rage. "I will have you know, sir, that I am very closely acquainted with Sir William!" And when he laughed at her and shook his dark head in disbelief, she forgot herself enough to say furiously, "I may even be going to marry him, so there!"

"Has he asked you to?"

"Yes, of course he . . ." She bit back her angry retort and tried, belatedly, to regain an air of frosty hauteur. "Perhaps you would be kind enought to tell me where Sir William resides?"

"Very good," he applauded, "but you should not let your eyes sparkle so delightfully. It quite ruins the effect."

"Sir, I asked you a question."

"So you did, ma'am. And did you really suppose that this house was Fossick's?"

"Well, naturally I did," returned Kitty tartly, "since the coachman whom I engaged to bring us here assured me that this was the place. Oh, it is too bad!" she exclaimed indignantly. "What can he have meant by it? He was surly enough, certainly, but I had not thought him a villain!"

The tall man did not seem to be sharing her outraged feelings. Indeed, he still had the appearance of a man who was greatly enjoying himself. He smiled at her again in a way that made her want to forget her dignity and hit him, and said, "I daresay you were in too much of a hurry again. It is useless to be in too much haste in Ireland, ma'am. Nothing is ever gained by it."

"It was not so at all," she returned coldly. "My directions to the man were perfectly explicit. I asked him to take us to Mount Comeragh, and he undertook to do so. Really, Mr. . . ."

"My name is Denny. I have already told you."

"I am afraid that I cannot properly attend to people who brandish firearms in my face," she said waspishly. "Well, Mr. Denny, you may tell me if you do not think it shocking that the coachman should be dishonest? Or are all Irish people lacking in honesty?"

"No more than the English, I should say."

He drew out his snuffbox, and when he had taken a pinch and inhaled it rather messily, so that a shower of snuff spilled itself down the front of his dark cloak, he added thoughtfully, "No. I would venture to say that we Irish are even a shade more honest than the English. We may enjoy deceiving others (particularly ladies from England who are in a hurry) but we seldom deceive ourselves as to our motives."

She ignored his provoking aside and said, "If this is not Mount Comeragh, will you tell me, please, where I may find it?"

"You see," he said, looking amused, "you have proved me right already. Your coachman has my sympathy."

Kitty flounced off the bed and stood up very straight. "Well, he has not mine! And he is about to discover it. He positively assured me that this is Mount Comeragh."

"And so it is."

Kitty gaped at him. "But you told me only an instant ago that this was not . . ."

"You should listen more carefully," he said, odiously kind.

"This is not Fossick's house. This is Mount Comeragh Castle, and Fossick's house goes by the name of Mount Comeragh Lodge." He looked down at her flushed, appalled face and added, "Do not look so stricken. It is a mere five miles up the river from here."

"Five miles!" repeated Kitty in a voice of weak dismay. "I shall never prevail upon that man to go so far tonight!" She turned away from him, battling with a strong tendency to burst into tears.

"Come," he said calmly, as if it were no great matter after all that she should be stranded in this moldering ruin. "I did not think you would be so easily defeated."

"Then see if you can prevail upon that man to take his horses out again!" she flared at him. "It is not only for myself that I am in despair. My maid and my son are with me, and Robert is unwell from the effects of the journey. It is always so," she added despondently. "He has been sickly since the day of his birth."

"And no wonder, if you treat him so. I will come and speak to this coachman of yours, however. There is no need for you to fret about it."

Kitty found herself saying haughtily, "There is no need for you to trouble yourself with my affairs, sir."

"No," he returned equably, "I daresay you would much prefer it if I rode off and left you here. By morning you will have an opportunity to indulge your taste for Gothic ruins to the full. With a little management, too, your child may be found to have contracted an inflammation of the lung, and your situation will have developed all the gratifying ingredients of a fashionable romance."

"Don't be ridiculous," said Kitty crossly. She added in a stifled tone, as though it hurt her to utter the words, "It is kind of you to help us, sir. It is true that Robert should be got into a warm bed. I am grateful, but if you would offer your help in a less odious manner, it would be easier for me to express my gratitude."

"Don't distress yourself," he replied indifferently, picking up the lantern. "I would do as much for any stray or derelict creature." He offered her his arm. "Shall we go, ma'am."

"I am not so derelict that I cannot walk by myself," she retorted, sweeping past him. "You may carry the lantern and show me the way."

Mr. Denny followed her out, and since he seemed to know his way about very well, it was not long before they emerged into the stable yard. The coachman came out of one of the loose-boxes and looked upon the tall gentleman with amazement and surly suspicion. "Holy saints preserve us!" he exclaimed, squinting up into the lantern light. "And who may this be?"

"You would do better to ask yourself how you are going to convey this lady to her destination," remarked Mr. Denny. He did not wait to see what effect his words might have had, but moved past the coachman into what appeared to be a harness room.

Here Martha was to be found, sitting rigidly upon an upturned corn measure with Robert tossing uneasily in her arms. Mr. Denny nodded to Martha and then turned aside to light Kitty's way through the doorway. The coachman stamped in and stood glowering.

For a moment there was no sound but Robert's cough and the soft stamping of horses' hooves from the loose-box nearby. Kitty was bracing herself for the moment when Martha's wrath would find its way into speech, but both her maid and the coachman appeared to be mesmerized by the tall gentleman who had suddenly appeared in their midst and was thoughtfully surveying them.

He turned at length to the coachman. "Could your horses go any farther tonight? As you will be aware, this is not the house to which this lady expected to be brought. They cannot stay here."

The coachman began to expostulate. His horses were tired, and no wonder, with the lady in such a fever to press on. One of them was lame, moreover, and that one could not go a step farther, no matter what.

Mr. Denny listened to this tirade without comment. He merely nodded from time to time in a tranquil way, and the coachman's manner, at first belligerent, began to change perceptibly. Perhaps it had suddenly dawned upon him that this tall gentleman was the owner of the gray thoroughbred that was stabled alongside his own tired nags, and was therefore someone worthy of respect. Whatever the reason, he ended up by giving it as his opinion that although his bay horse was very lame, the roan could be ridden a small piece farther.

"But how delightful!" cried Kitty in a voice of spurious rapture. "Shall we all mount the roan horse at the same time? Or shall we take turns to walk?"

"You may have the roan for yourself, ma'am," said Mr. Denny dismissively. "I shall take your little boy up in front of me and I will send for your maid as soon as I have the child safe and warm."

"Oh, no, you will not!" said Martha fiercely. "This is a sick child, sir! There's going to be no more jauntering about for him this day!" She turned to Kitty and hissed ferociously, "Now you listen to me, milady! Robert's in no fit state to be moved about any more this day! Did I not tell you that we should have waited until Sir William sent his carriage for us?"

"You have said it so many times, Martha, that I have no wish to hear it again."

"Someone must try to talk sense into you, milady," said Martha doggedly. She turned to Mr. Denny as if seeking support. "Such a journey as we've had, sir! Hurry, hurry, day after day! It's a wonder this poor little mite has anything left inside him, so sick he's been. And he's in a fever, too, or my name's not Martha Barley! Can you not speak to her Ladyship, sir? She may attend to you."

"I doubt it," said Mr. Denny, glancing at Kitty momentarily with a dark, gleaming, mocking look. "We would be better to take your advice and get this child into a warm bed without delay," he added, walking across to Martha. "He would be well wrapped up in my cloak, and I can have him safe between the sheets in thirty minutes. Will you not trust me with him for a little while?"

If Kitty had not been so tired, she might have enjoyed the way Mr. Denny brought Martha round his finger with such ease, and she might have marveled at the way he had the coachman actually bustling to do his bidding. As it was, she had no feeling left in her. In a daze she heard Mr. Denny ordering this and that to be done, and watched him as he bent his head and listened with every appearance of rapt attention to Martha' injunctions and instructions.

Martha was not inclined to look on the male sex (with the exception of Robert, of course) with any favor. Even poor Johnny her husband—had been known to retreat under the lash of Martha's tongue, while Wandlebury (understandably even lower in Martha's estimation than Kitty's late husband had ever been) had declared that he was all in a quake whenever he heard Martha's tread upon the stairs. Mr. Denny showed no signs of quaking, and Martha and he might almost have been acquaintances of long standing by the time they were ready to ride off.

An ancient sidesaddle had been brought down from the wall of the harness room, where it must have been gathering mold and cobwebs for an age, and the roan was saddled with this. It was exceedingly uncomfortable, and Kitty's traveling gown, a narrow-skirted, high-waisted affair in dark blue cloth, was not designed for riding on horseback. However, she had no choice but to hitch it up as best she could, and to drape her fur-lined cloak over the unseemly jumble of skirts and pommel and legs and ankles in their elegant black and white half-boots. She drew the hood of her cloak over her disheveled curls and kept her head stiffly averted as Mr. Denny checked the makeshift girths, and did not look at him again until he had turned to take Robert from Martha's arms.

"Do not be worried for him," she heard him say. "He will be taken the greatest care of, and your mistress too, and you will be sent for directly."

He led Kitty down a long avenue of trees, past a ruined lodge, and turned uphill into the gusty darkness. The hill was steep and the ground uneven. Gorse bushes loomed up suddenly at intervals, so that Kitty's horse swerved nervously away from them and all but threw her off on two occasions. There was no moon, and the higher they rode the stronger grew the roaring of the gale.

At long last they breasted the top of the hill, and as the ground sloped down before them on the other side, the wind ceased as though it had been shut off by an invisible door. Kitty could hear the keening of it up above, but in their sudden haven of shelter it was quiet and tolerably calm. Below her she saw the welcome glimmer of lights among the trees, and as they jolted on toward these, the roan must have felt something of the same exultation and relief, for he broke into a bouncing canter. She came up alongside Mr. Denny for the first time since they set out. Robert was lying quite still in his arms, apparently asleep.

She said with a trace of awkwardness, "I do not care to think what would have become of us without your help, sir."

"I daresay you would have contrived well enough," he replied.

"Indeed, no." She knew that he was laughing at her efforts to thank him, yet she felt bound to persevere. "Well, if you will not accept thanks for your kindness, I shall leave it to Sir William. He will be able to convince you that we stand in your debt."

"You think so?"

"I am sure of it." She refused to be daunted by his non-committal tone. William would set all to rights for her: he was never at a loss for the proper thing to say. "What a din those dogs are making!" she exclaimed as they came nearer to the house. "William's household will not fail to hear us coming."

"My good girl," he retorted mockingly, "why must you imagine that every dwelling place you come to is inhabited by Fossick? Are you besotted with the fellow? There was never any question of your going to his house tonight. This is Dennystown, and it belongs to me."

CHAPTER THREE

THE LONG ROOM where the Denny family spent most of their leisure hours (illogically named the morning room) was lit at night by branches of candles and warmed and rendered glowing and delightful by a great fire of turfs and logs at one end. Close to the fire, nodding over her sewing, sat Miss Biddy Denny. She was dressed in black, her thin face almost extinguished by a well-starched cap. Even when half asleep Miss Biddy's air of good sense did not desert her, nor did her tiny form relax from its upright position on her chair.

The two other occupants of the morning room were in the throes of an argumentative game of chess. Mick Denny, a lanky young man of about twenty years of age, with dark hair cut into modishly wind-swept locks and a neckcloth so high that he could hardly turn his head, was hotly disputing his small sister's right to take his bishop. She, on the other hand, was holding the captive prelate in a firm grasp and had no intention of giving him back.

Mary Denny was twelve years old. She was a skinny little girl, as dark as the rest of her family, but with no sign, yet, of their handsomeness. The Denny nose, which lent such a commanding air to her brothers, was far too large for Mary's sallow little face. It was the bane of her life, Mary's nose, and at one time she was in the habit of praying every night for a miracle that would make it grow smaller. She no longer prayed for this miracle, she had lost heart, and besides, Father James had told her that it was wrong to pray for such worldly things, she should be grateful for an attribute which saved her from the sin of vanity. Mary would have given anything to be beautiful, but what she lacked in that respect she made up for in determination.

"No," she was saying firmly, "it was quite fair, and I won't give him back."

"Then we'd better stop playing," said Mick curtly. "I do not play games with you if you cheat. Why, even Shamus plays fair . . ."

"Shamus does not play chess. He is not old enough . . ."

"What is that to say to it? Put that bishop back, Mary."

At that moment the door was flung open and a small boy with red hair rushed in.

"Miss Biddy! Miss Biddy!" he cried shrilly. "Denny has come in with a lady and a little boy, and he says you're to come at once to the south room!" The little boy, who might have been about seven years old, was dressed in nankeen trousers and a plain linen shirt which was anything but clean. His shock of bright red hair stood up round his head, giving him a startled air. He ran up to Miss Biddy and shook her arm. He was in a high state of excitement. "Denny says to come at once!"

"Wh . . . where did you say they are, Shamus!" demanded Miss Biddy, putting a hand to her cap and betraying only by the sharpness of her voice that she had been taken by surprise. "Do not tell me, child, that you have dirtied that shirt already? It is the second one you've had on today! And it is past your bedtime . . ."

"Please, Miss Biddy, make haste! He's taken the little boy to the south room," said Shamus, giving his dirty shirt a perfunctory wipe with his hand. "And he was as red as Father James's nose when Denny took the wrappings off him!"

Miss Biddy was like a small blackbird, the way she flitted so silently and quickly about her tasks in the house. Shamus scampered to hold the door for her, following her very quickly as though fearful of being brought back into the room. Mick had, indeed, intended to lay hands on Shamus, and as the door shut determinedly, he said, "Deuce take the little devil. He's harder to catch than an eel."

"If I had played with Shamus instead of playing chess," said Mary wistfully, "I should know what is going on. Whom do you think Luke has brought back with him?"

They fell to guessing who the mysterious visitors might be, and Mary's guesses grew so wild that Mick said scornfully, "Do not be so silly. We will find out in good time."

"I would like to march upstairs and find out. I've a good mind to. Why must Shamus be the one to get all the treats? He should have been in bed hours ago. Luke is monstrously unfair, the way he allows Shamus to do as he likes. I've a mind to tell him so . . ."

"You've a mind to tell me what?" inquired Luke from the doorway. He had shed his long cloak and was clad in breeches and boots and a coat of some dark brown cloth. His appearance was scarcely elegant, even slovenly, for he had no patience with tying neckcloths in intricate folds and wore a narrow cravat which he had twisted negligently into a knot at his throat, and his coat was worn at the cuffs. Mick, who had adopted a highly modish style of dress since his brief visit to London, thought his brother's appearance positively dowdy, but all his efforts to make him change his ways had met with failure. Luke wore his clothes as a covering, no more, and he cared not at all if his waistcoat was marked with mud or grease or if his coat needed mending. For all that, however, he was a distinguished figure. His shoulders were broad, and with his great height and the confident angle at which he held his dark head, he had the air of a man who knew where he was going.

He walked up to Mary and looked down at her gravely, "What is it that you wish to tell me?"

She tried to gaze coolly back at him but looked merely apprehensive.

He said softly, "You should be more careful to lower your voice if you do not wish to be overheard. And another thing: you are not going to go near the south room. Is that clear?"

She nodded.

"And for your comfort," he added, smiling, "you may like to know that Shamus was dispatched to his bed an hour ago."

"Oh!" This information must have made Mary feel more herself, for she demanded, "Why may I not go near the south room?"

"There is a child there with a fever. I do not want to have an epidemic through the house."

"Oh!" Mick and Mary eyed each other, each waiting for the other to ask the question uppermost in their minds.

Luke balanced his snuffbox upon the palm of one hand and opened it. He inhaled a pinch of snuff and watched them with narrowed eyes.

Mick, meeting that glance, said lightly, "How pleased

Aunt Biddy will be to have a sickroom to preside over! Is this child very ill?"

"Too ill to be moved at present, I should say. For all his fond mother's determination to quit Dennystown in the morning, I do not think they will do so. Not unless she leaves without her child, and that might take more effrontery than even her Ladyship is capable of. You, Mick, will have to put forward your best efforts to make her visit supportable. It will be more in your line than mine, I fancy, though I found her diverting enough this evening." He watched the bewilderment on their faces with keen enjoyment and waited for the questions which must surely come.

"Who in the world is it, then?"

"Why is she a Ladyship?"

"You're roasting us!"

"Is the little boy hers?"

"Oh, take no notice of him, Mary," said Mick at last. "You can see from Luke's face it is nothing but a hum."

"On the contrary," said Luke. "I am perfectly serious."

"Oh, have done! Luke! Who is this female?"

Luke seated himself in a chair by the chess table and began to toy idly with one of the ivory pawns. He looked them over indulgently and said, "This female, as you call her, is a remarkable and enterprising member of her sex. She is on her way to visit William Fossick at the Lodge; in fact, I rather understand that she means to marry our energetic sheriff. They should be well matched. When I found the lady first she was hunting for Fossick among the cobwebs at the Castle." He threw back his head and laughed aloud. "Oh, they should be an entertaining pair. I wish Fossick joy of her . . ."

"Fossick?" exclaimed Mick. "Looking for Fossick at the Castle? Why, he's not set foot there since . . ." He stopped

(38)

abruptly, glanced at Mary, and said, "Well, damn it! Why should this idiotish female expect to find him there?"

Luke shrugged his shoulders. "She must have told the coachman to take her to Mount Comeragh, and he chose (out of cussedness perhaps) to take her to the Castle. Perhaps Fossick did not give the lady very precise instruction," he added, controlling the laughter in his voice with difficulty. "It appears that Fossick forgot to send his carriage to meet her Ladyship at Waterford. No doubt all his troubles over Kelagher's escape have made him forgetful; so this masterful lady hired a coach in Waterford, and when she was set down at the Castle in the dark and the rain, she found that the coachman would go no farther."

"And what were you doing there?" asked Mary curiously.

"Looking for banshees, my child," said Luke.

"You have told me often and often that there are no such things," Mary complained.

"Well, let us say that it is none of your business, shall we?"

"Never mind that," said Mick impatiently. "Who is this lady? And what happened to her at the Castle?"

"Well, she decided to spend the night inside the Castle. I told you she was a strong-minded female, did I not? She also has a most fertile imagination, for she no sooner saw me than she took me for one of Fossick's mad or bad kinsmen. Thank you, Mick," he added, as his brother emitted a sudden explosive exclamation. "It was rather startling, was it not? By heaven, though," he added reminiscently, "if I had indeed been a violent lunatic, I believe she would have tried to outface me!"

"But who is she?"

"She tells me that she is the Lady Katherine Harcombe." He threw a quizzical look at Mick, who was looking perfectly dumbfounded, and added, "Yes. You are right. It is none other than the famous Lady Kitty herself. But there is really no need for you to stand there with your mouth open like a stranded fish. I do not think her Ladyship would admire you in that pose."

"But . . . but . . ."

"I have never heard of this lady," said Mary bluntly. "Why is she so famous?"

"Now that you ask me," replied Luke, ignoring Mick's ribald smirk, "I do not seem to be able to remember the reason. I dare say it is because she has such a prodigious number of bonnets."

"So many indiscretions, you mean," said Mick knowledgeably. "I remember when I was in London, it was all over the town that Wandlebury . . ."

"Keep your reminiscences for another time, will you?" Luke turned his back upon his brother and smiled down at Mary's entranced face. "You will have to play hostess for me, child. Aunt Biddy has taken over the sickroom, and we all know what that means. I do not think we will see much of her until she has nursed that child through his fever. So, you see . . ."

"Mary play hostess to Kitty Harcombe!" exclaimed Mick scornfully. "I hardly think that exchanging chit-chat with children, especially with Mary, who can think of nothing but her pony, is much in her Ladyship's line. She will go mad with boredom in half an hour."

"You think so?" Luke's tone was chill. "Mary will entertain her very well, I don't doubt, and if her Ladyship is not pleased with us here, let us hope that she has the conduct to hide her feelings until her child is well enough to be removed."

"Oh, I do not think that hiding her feelings is in Lady Kitty's line, either," Mick said, safe in the knowledge that his brother had never before laid eyes on the scandalous widow.

(40)

He looked up as he spoke, and met a rather penetrating glance from Luke's dark eyes which caused him to say hastily, "But of course I only know what I have heard about her. I never saw her except at a distance. She was very beautiful and seemed always to be laughing," he added wistfully. "Did you not think her very lovely?"

"Doubtless when she is cleaned and tidied a bit, she will be passable."

"Passable!" echoed Mick. "Why, there would be half a dozen men in town who would call you out for speaking of Kitty Harcombe so slightingly." He looked pityingly at his ignorant brother and added, "It is not really even for her indiscretions that she is truly famous, you know. She is quite the rage, an accredited beauty, and all the ladies try to copy her clothes and the way she does her hair. None of them succeed in doing so, though, for her hair is like molten gold . . ."

"We will make a poet of you yet," said Luke dryly.

Mick sighed. "You're hopeless. I shall give up trying to convert you, and I don't suppose Lady Kitty will care. She has dozens of admirers already."

"When may we see her?" asked Mary.

"In the morning."

"What in the world can Kitty Harcombe want with Fossick?" demanded Mick suddenly.

"Why don't you ask her?" suggested Luke in a disinterested tone. "Or better still, ask Fossick when he comes here to see her?"

"Fossick coming here? Good God! You don't mean to ask that fellow to Dennystown? Why, next you'll be inviting our illustrious cousin, Comeragh, to dine!"

"Hardly that," said Luke, smiling faintly. "The old man would think it was an attempt to poison him. He imagines that I can hardly wait to step into his shoes, as it is."

Mick laughed. Since the death of Harry St. Dennis, Luke was next in line to inherit his distant kinsman's earldom. It had become a matter of amusement to the Denny brothers to observe how some neighbors, who had once scarcely deigned to recognize them, had lately become amazingly affable. It was almost equally diverting to know that old Lord Comeragh would certainly have done anything in his power to prevent Luke from inheriting anything that was his. However, jesting about old Lord Comeragh's tantrums was one thing. To invite Sir William Fossick to Dennystown seemed to Mick to be quite another.

He reiterated in an incredulous tone, "Surely, there's no need to ask that pompous fellow here?"

"Why, certainly," replied Luke. "If Lady Kitty is to be our guest, I can scarcely do less than inform Fossick that she is here." He glanced momentarily at Mary again, before adding, "Shamus had best go off to Father James in the morning."

"Oh, not again!" expostulated Mary. She encountered a distinctly frosty glance from Luke's dark eyes, and faltered. "Indeed, Luke, he dislikes it so, being sent away whenever anyone comes . . ."

Luke shrugged. "You had best be off to bed, Mary. I'm in no humor to be argued with."

Mary opened her mouth as if about to say something, but a glance at her elder brother's face made her think better of it and with a gulp she flounced out of the room.

"Little minx," Luke said when the door closed behind her. "She is getting too saucy for her own good."

"Surely," said Mick, "there can be no harm in Kitty Harcombe seeing Shamus? Do you not think you are being over-careful that no one should see him?"

"Perhaps. I prefer not to invite trouble."

"But what trouble could there be? It is to the highest

degree unlikely that Fossick would remember Shamus, or even be interested if he did."

"Unlikely, I agree."

"And after all, it is more than a year since Shamus first came here. Is he never going to be allowed to show his face when we have company?" Mick looked curiously across at Luke's impassive face. He added, half derisively, "Anyone would suppose that you thought Shamus was in danger!"

"The boy is just beginning to settle down," Luke said in reply. "I do not want him overset by the sight of Fossick's red-coated ruffians."

"Good lord! Don't tell me Fossick still keeps his private army at Mount Comeragh Lodge? I had thought, since the Amnesty, that things had come back to normal."

Luke smiled thinly. "So people say. Our energetic sheriff still keeps his state, however. How else should he hope to recapture Kelagher, or lay the villainous Green Man by the heels?"

Mick gave vent to a crack of laughter. "How I wish I'd seen Fossick's face when Kelagher got away!"

CHAPTER FOUR

STRANGERS did not often come to Dennystown. The house was hardly easy to get to, being built on the sparsely inhabited side of a range of hills which guarded the town of Clonmel on the southeast side. It was not thought to be a place where any gentleman of taste would choose to live.

The Dennys, who by their stubborn adherence to the popish church had suffered many of the privations and disabilities of the old Penal Laws, had no choice in the matter. But no one envied them their outlandish hillside dwelling. Most sensible people chose to live in the broad valley of the River Suir, where the green meadows and the rolling wooded slopes made a prosperous and delightful setting for their houses. From there they could stroll in their gardens and drive about their well-laid-out parks and admire the ever-changing panorama of the distant blue hills; infinitely more desirable than living up in the hills themselves, as the poor Dennys did, and having to ride five miles over the wild moors before coming in sight of civilization. Wheeled vehicles were obliged to go round by the boggy and rocky road for more than twenty miles, and if the ladies of Dennystown wished to visit the town of Clonmel, it was a tedious journey for them.

The poor people of the district, however, were very well able to find their way to the long, low gray house upon the hill. Many of them, even from quite far away, were used to looking on the Dennystown people as belonging in some measure to themselves. The large shabby kitchen was a meeting place and a refuge for any who might come, and hardly a day went by without some call upon Miss Biddy's nursing skill or without Luke being asked to arbitrate over some dispute or other. The master of Dennystown might be thought less than perfect by some, his casual appearance and unconciliating manners made him less than a favorite with others, but to the country people Denny was a king in all but name.

Local legends told of the golden days when a Denny had been able to stand upon a high peak of the Comeragh hills and claim all the land in sight. Luke laughed at these legends and said that they were fairy tales, but even he did not deny that the mountainous stretch of land which was now his property was only a fragment of what had once been in the family possession. There were very few Catholic families with even the same modest degree of wealth as theirs, and Luke said that it was better to let the old songs stay unsung and the tales untold, lest others should choose to remember the more recent times when Luke's grandfather had followed a defeated Stuart king into exile. Then it had been that a younger brother, less romantically inclined and with a better appreciation of what counted in life, had been rewarded for his loyalty to Farmer George by the gift of his disgraced brother's lands. This younger brother had prospered, had turned his back upon the old faith in favor of the new, and when in the course of time he had been rewarded with an earldom, he had changed his family's name from plain Denny to the rather more illustrious-sounding St. Dennis. Thus it was that in terms of worldy wealth the Dennystown Dennys were the poor relations of the great Lord Comeragh at Kilnabawn, and there was no love lost between the two houses. But no degree of poverty or persecution could wean the country people from their legacy of songs and stories, and they persisted in treating the family at Dennystown as minor royalty and tended to look to them for guidance and support.

Luke, as head of the family, was the focus of a fervent, though by no means constant, adulation. At the time of the latest and most dangerous threat of a French invasion, the gentlemen of the county had been asked to raise men to defend Ireland from the invaders. A huge throng of volunteers had forthwith appeared at Dennystown, all breathing fire and patriotism and swearing undying attachment to Denny and to King George, in about that order of priority. At the head of the vast concourse of people, Luke had ridden down the mountain to place himself at the disposal of the commander at Clonmel.

All this was somewhat to the chagrin of other gentlemen who had promised to bring a substantial number of recruits, and had been obliged to resort to bribery and threats to gather enough followers. They murmured against Luke among themselves, fully expecting him to become quite overweening and intolerable as a result of all this acclaim. Sir William Fossick was heard to say grimly that there would be no holding Denny now. If the Whigs got back into power and the Catholics were given the political rights which they had been clamoring for, they would soon find that Ireland was to be governed by nothing but Denny and his like. Once one of them got in a position of influence, there would be dozens of them there as well, for those papists, Sir William warned, would stop at nothing to help one another. One could see, he said, that Denny would not easily return to the role of an insignificant Catholic gentleman once he had been given a taste for power. From the look of him, you would think he fancied himself as a prince.

No one had taken a great deal of notice to what Sir William said, for everyone knew that he was Lord Comeragh's man, and it was only natural that he would think and say the worst about Denny. And it turned out that the deputy sheriff was wrong.

When the French invasion came to nothing, the recruits had gone back to their homes, some of them managing to purloin a gun or two, and things at Dennystown went back to their normal humdrum pattern. Luke and his erstwhile adherents resumed their relationship of landlord and tenant, and from being a popular leader, he was reduced to a mere man to whom they owed rent and service.

What was worse, he was a landlord who would interfere in their affairs if he thought fit, and within three months of his most triumphant hour as a leader of men, Luke was nearly murdered when he stopped some of his people from tying the hated tithe proctor to a stake and setting fire to his clothes.

Even looking back on it, the peasants thought it unreasonable of Himself to interfere. As a good Christian gentleman he must surely feel the injustice of having to pay good money to a heretic church. But when the heat of their rage was over, and their fury had turned to laughter at the sight of the tithe proctor galloping off in his singed clothes as though the hounds of hell were after him, they were ashamed that they had turned upon Himself. Not that the tithe proctor wouldn't have been better for a roasting; he was a wicked divil, sure enough, and burning was too good for him. But they had not meant to turn upon Denny.

They gathered round him sheepishly and let him lecture them on the need to use only lawful means to fight injustice, glancing nervously at the stout stick which was all he had possessed to defend himself against their pitchforks and spades. Any violent action, taken without the sanction of the law, he told them, could only lead to disaster. They let him speak, but their eyes slid away from his, for in their hearts they knew that Himself was wrong. Every sensible man knew that the law was only for the Protestant rulers who held sway over them. It was useless for Denny and Father James to try to tell them that there would be justice and a better way of life for them if they would only be patient and wait. They had waited too long already, most people felt, and things were getting worse rather than better.

The joint influence of Luke and Father James was considerable, but the doctrines they preached were too unpopular, too much out of joint with the spirit of the times. They might as well have tried to hold back a tidal wave as to hope to stem the upsurge of militant feeling which was to come to a head in the summer of 1798.

The uprising came and went. In County Tipperary, at least, the trouble never grew into anything of major military significance, but to the poor people who lived through those bloody, terror-stricken months, it was not so easily forgotten.

From the earliest months of that distressing year, platoons of red-coated soldiers (many of them hired mercenaries from abroad) roamed about looking for arms, for seditious documents, for anything which might be suspect. If the householders did not surrender all they had at once, their homes would be burned by the military. Even the wearing of a green riband might be taken as a sign of disaffection, and dozens of persons who had never so much as dreamed of rebellion were dragged into prison and left there for weeks.

The high sheriff, Mr. Thomas Judkin-Fitzgerald, had openly threatened to flog and hang the spirit of disaffection out of the county; and if he punished ten innocent people to every one who was guilty, he thought himself justified in doing so. Everywhere there was alarm and helpless fury and despair, violence begetting violence on every side; and though in Tipperary the uprising in its military sense was crushed almost before it had begun, no one but the most determined Tories could feel much satisfaction in the victory. There was a horrid feeling of distrust and danger in the air even after a year had gone by.

The sheriff and his deputies were still very much on the alert, still given to setting out on punitive excursions on the most slender information. No one knew when his name might not be brought to Sir William Fossick's notice, and when his turn might come to be examined as to his loyalty. Law-abiding people felt that it was wiser to stay at home and to talk to no one, for there was no telling what the next few days might not bring forth.

This was the state of things when Kitty Harcombe came into Ireland, but she knew nothing of such things and would not have believed the half of them if she had been told. Her Ladyship came from another world, where it did not do to take anything too seriously and where even the topic of the war with France was treated with cynicism and mockery. It was all the rage, at that time, to admire the enemy and to dress after the fashion of the French ladies. Bonaparte, of course, was a monster, and one trusted to dear Lord Nelson to defeat him in time, but that did not mean that it was possible, in the meantime, to do without the exquisite gauzes and muslins and ribbons which only the Parisians seemed to be able to make, and Kitty would have felt herself dowdy indeed if she had not been able to procure silk stockings and gloves and all manner of fripperies from France to adorn her person.

When she woke up on the morning after her arrival at Dennystown, however, it would have been hard to imagine anything more peaceful and quiet than the great damask-hung bed in which she was lying. She opened her eyes and stretched her white, slender arms outside the sheets, feeling stiff and sore yet strangely tranquil in spirit.

After a while, when the clouding effects of sleep had receded, she began to recall the events of the previous day. Her memory of the last part of it was confused. There had been so many people turning out to meet them in the cobbled forecourt of the house, and Robert had woken up and begun to cry for Martha.

The crowd of servants had swarmed forward to help her (at least she supposed they must be servants, though few of them wore livery and were mostly even more unkempt than their master). There had been a wizened old man who had helped her to dismount and who had spoken to Mr. Denny in the most familiar terms, wondering aloud why he had been out so long and had missed his dinner.

Once dismounted from her uncomfortable seat, Kitty had been led into a warm, rambling house. Mr. Denny preceded her through a maze of passages, and then all at once she found herself blinking dazedly in a charming, candlelit hall. She had little time to look about her, for Robert was by this time sobbing wildly. While she tried to soothe him, she had noticed a little red-haired boy darting to meet them, and there had been a pack of spaniels who yapped and fawned upon them all the way up the shallow, curving staircase.

Finally they had come to a large bedroom, where Kitty,

breathless from struggling with her screaming child, had dumped him down upon a high four-poster bed. Mr. Denny, odious man, had allowed her to snatch Robert out of his arms in the hall and had followed her up the stairs without offering to take him back again. Kitty tried vainly to calm him, but the child was hysterical and would not be comforted, and she was not sure whether to be glad or sorry when a small tornado of a lady swept into the room just in time to see her shake Robert in an attempt to quiet him. The little lady took Robert firmly into her arms, saying, "There! There! Miss Biddy's got you safely, you little dote. Just have a nice cry, and then you shall have some milk and go to sleep."

"There is no need to encourage him to cry," said Kitty in a nettled tone. "And if you give him milk, he will probably be sick. He has kept no food in him all day . . ."

"Better to leave him to Aunt Biddy, ma'am," advised Luke from the doorway. And at her haughty, inquiring look he added, "Let me make you known to my aunt, Miss Bridget Denny. Aunt Biddy, this is Lady Katherine Harcombe."

Kitty inclined her head coolly.

"This child is in a fever," announced Miss Biddy, ignoring her. "He must be got into bed. Bridie, have you put the warming pan in the bed? Well, do so at once, if you please! Have your wits been taken from you? And go and find Agnes-Mary and tell her to look out flannel and cherry cordial and a small size in bed shifts. We put them away when Shamus grew too large. She will know the ones I mean. And you, Maura, go to the stillroom . . ."

Miss Biddy's directions flowed on. Her voice was low and matter of fact, and Robert, apparently mesmerised by this lady in the enormous mobcap who had taken such a firm hold on his affairs, had lolled back against her shoulder, sobbing in a spasmodic, spent way. From time to time Miss Biddy said

(51)

something to him, using just the same tone of voice as that in which she issued her orders to the maids.

Kitty stood beside her, feeling very foolish and helpless, a sensation she neither liked nor was accustomed to. Nor was it made any better by the knowledge that her discomfiture was giving Luke considerable amusement. She said in an exasperated tone, "I suppose he must have caught cold in that abominable carriage. I should never have brought him."

"No, indeed, you should not," said Miss Biddy, speaking to her for the first time and calmly brushing by her to carry Robert to a low chair by the fire. "For you appear to have no idea of how to look after him. Yes, Maura, set that basin down beside me, if you please. What this child needs now is peace and quiet. Luke, take her Ladyship to the pink room. I trust that Bridie will have made it ready by now, and she will attend to her wants."

"My maid is being sent for, I believe," said Kitty stiffly. "And you need not trouble yourself over my son, ma'am. I am not so weary that I cannot attend to him myself."

"You will fret him," said Miss Biddy. "And when your maid arrives, to be sure I will see that she is sent to you. Leave your little boy to me. I know just what is best for him."

"You had better do as Aunt Biddy tells you," said Luke, smiling rather maliciously. "We all do, you know."

"I prefer to see that Robert . . ."

"Come," he said, taking her arm and drawing her inexorably toward the door. "He is in good hands, I assure you."

"Well, really!" exclaimed Kitty when she had been all but dragged out of the room and into the corridor. "Anyone would think that I was no more than a child myself!"

Luke ushered her into another firelit bedchamber, where a red-faced maid was curtsying and smiling. "Never mind," he said with odious kindness. "We are all of us inclined to behave like children when we are weary. Think no more

(52)

about it." He bowed to her, his dark eyes perfectly grave for a change, and left her.

Kitty had been only too glad to forget her chagrin and to submit to Bridie's rather rough-and-ready ministrations. A bath before the fire and a plate of cold meats upon a tray were all she wanted in the world just then, and afterward she tumbled into the large curtained bed and sank into a well of sleep. Somewhere in the middle of her first dark slumber she knew that Martha had arrived in the room and had stood over her. But she had been in no state to cope with a scolding from her maid and so had feigned sleep.

She was just wondering about Martha and how she did when Martha herself came in through the bedroom door. She was carrying a tray.

"Well, milady," she said in militant tones, "a fine thing this is."

"Oh, Martha," murmured Kitty sleepily, "I am prodigiously glad to see you. And how delicious that chocolate smells. I declare I am ravenous."

"I have brought you some bread and butter. Funny dark stuff the bread is, but it looks quite wholesome . . ."

Kitty found the bread and butter most reviving, and with her mouth full she asked her maid if she had had an uncomfortable journey over the hill to Dennystown.

"The less said about that the better," retorted Martha, plainly intending to expand upon the subject at length. "It's a wonder I've a bone left unbroken in my whole body! So rattled and shook I was, milady, you'll never credit it. It was not even a carriage they put me in, but a great barbarous thing with no wheels, more like a horse-drawn tea tray than anything else I've seen. I could hardly believe it when they told me that I was expected to ride in it. In fact, if it hadn't been for the thought of that poor fatherless child . . ."

"How is Robert this morning?"

Martha sniffed. "He's asleep now, as it happens."

"Thank heaven for that!"

"Poor little love! He was tossing and turning half the night, and crying out in his sleep. If you'd taken my advice in the first place, milady, we would have been spared a great deal of trouble. What's more, we wouldn't find ourselves mewed up in these outlandish hills, dependent upon the charity of a lot of papists."

"Papists?" murmured Kitty, sipping her chocolate. "And what is so terrible about that?"

Martha retorted darkly that her Ladyship ought to know what she meant. Were not papists as bad as foreigners? And foreigners, these days, were mostly Frenchies, and spies at that!

Kitty gave vent to a little hiccup of laughter. "So you think our dark sinister deliverer is a French spy, do you? And I merely supposed him to be a robber! Famous!" This notion was so refreshing that Kitty was able to suffer the next chapter of Martha's complaints with suitable meekness, and her irritation did not well up again until her maid mentioned for the third time that that meddling Miss Denny had been giving Robert all manner of dangerous potions and that she really did not deem it safe to leave her darling out of her sight.

"Well, go and stand over him!" she told Martha crossly. "You will not have to guard him for very long, for doubtless Sir William will be arriving posthaste as soon as he knows we are here. And I am persuaded that he would never try to put you in anything but a very proper four-wheeled carriage. William prides himself upon his well-sprung carriages. I particularly remember him prosing on about them in his letters."

"I'm not leaving here until Robert's fever is gone,

milady," retorted Martha. "I've put up with too many of your crazy starts. I'll not allow you to murder your son."

"But you were only telling me just now that he was in danger of being murdered by Miss Denny's potions," Kitty teased. "And besides, you were lamenting at being mewed up here with all these wicked papists . . ."

"Don't try your blandishing ways on me," said Martha, visibly softened but determined to cling to her point. "Robert will not be fit to leave for several days, and if he develops one of his putrid sore throats, I do not know when he will be better. If Sir William comes, he will have to wait until the child is better. And I daresay he will, for he was a nice, kind, patient gentleman, from what I remember."

"Good heavens, Martha! I did not know he was in your good books. What has he done to deserve this?"

"He behaves like a gentleman should and treats your Ladyship wiith proper respect," said Martha stiffly. "Which is more than I can say for that Lord Wandlebury."

"We will not discuss Lord Wandlebury, Martha. And do not sniff in that horrid way, if you please. The way my friends treat me is entirely my own affair."

"There's some that take advantage, though, and some that don't," Martha said with the exasperating familiarity of an old retainer. "And whatever your Ladyship may pretend about wishing to remain your own mistress, it'll be a good day when you decide to settle down and have a man to look after you again." And with this parting shot, she seized upon Kitty's denuded breakfast tray and bore it out of the room.

Kitty sighed and her mouth took on a wry twist. Martha clung to the old myth that Johnny Harcombe had been all that a good solid husband should be, and as time went on, so did his virtues increase. Nor was there any quelling her once she decided to voice her opinion that Kitty should get married again and put an end to her present giddy existence. A husband, in Martha's view, was to be a cure for all ills; and doubtless she now entertained hopes of Kittty accepting Sir William's offer of marriage. On the face of it, Kitty conceded, it was only reasonable that Martha should be hopeful. Why otherwise should they have come all this way?

As it happened, Kitty had been so taken up with the trials and discomforts of their journey that she had not yet fully examined her own intentions. Or had she merely avoided thinking of them? Should she accept William's offer? She did not know. She did not love him, but then she did not expect or look for love.

Once she had loved Johnny Harcombe. She had been seventeen when she married him, and she had given her whole heart to the gay, handsome young man who was to be her bridegroom. He and his modish, chattering crowd of friends had seemed like brilliant beings from another world to the country-bred Kitty, and it was only after the wedding that she began to learn that Johnny had been virtually forced to marry her by his family and that he regarded her with boredom.

He only came near her when he was drunk enough to bear the idea of sharing her bed, and when he found that her inexperienced embraces did not please him, he would rain insults upon her, reproach her for her insipid, countrified ways, and often enough would fling out of the house in search of better company. He never struck her; he had a horror of physical violence. But he might just as well have done so, for Kitty in her first dumb, bewildered misery was a helpless target for his cruel tongue.

But those early days of torment did not last forever. Kitty was young and inexperienced, but she was not spiritless. Before a year was out she had grown into a very different being from the green-eyed innocent whom Johnny Harcombe had married.

She learned to dress with style and elegance, and in time Kitty became the rage of the town. She not only became a beauty, but also learned to show the world a laughing face, to cut a dash in the right circles.

She and Johnny saw little of each other except in company, but they became known as one of the most expensive and dashing couples in society. Kitty even suspected, at the last, that Johnny was becoming quite proud of her; and with a baby son, a house in Brook Street which was a meeting place for all the gayest fashionables on the town, even the most disapproving of the Harcombe relations began to believe that Johnny's young wife was going to be the making of him.

In this they were mistaken, for Johnny overturned his curricle one night and broke his neck; but if Kitty was not destined to be the making of him, at least Johnny had played a large part in shaping her own character and destiny. She had come a long way in those three years of marriage, and the breaking of those first tender illusions had hurt quite damnably. Never again did she intend to give her heart away; never would she allow herself to be at the mercy of any man. Of that she was wholly determined. To achieve happiness it was necessary to expect nothing from anyone, to give no confidences and to take nothing too seriously. This was Kitty's philosophy, and until the sudden debacle of the Wandlebury scandal, it had served her very well.

So what was she to do about William? He was so very adoring, and though she did not place much dependence upon the lasting properties of any man's adoration, she thought she would always be able to handle him. He would be utterly dependable, too. There would be no more frantic, disorganized journeyings once she was William's wife. Everything would be arranged and provided for down to the smallest detail.

Perhaps Martha was right in thinking that she needed a man to look after her. It was an alluring thought after her recent adventures. She could do with a little cosseting and spoiling after the somewhat cavalier treatment she had received at the hands of that insolent, mocking, unpredictable Mr. Denny.

She lay back among her pillows and recalled how he had first appeared so suddenly and silently, a dangerous menacing figure in the darkness of the doorway. She could not help wondering what he had been doing there in the first place. It would not surprise her to learn that he had been mixed up in some wild and nefarious plot, though anything more laughably removed from her notion of a French spy she could scarcely imagine. Still, there had been a recklessness about his demeanor. She did not think that he would scruple to break the law if it seemed good to him, and though he had turned off her question as to whom he had expected to meet in the Castle, he need not think she was no longer interested. She fully intended to find out more.

She smiled to herself as Mr. Denny's dark, saturnine features rose vividly to her mind. He was not handsome at all, she decided, and his dress was positively shabby; yet for all that, he was a vital, dangerously attractive man. It would be amusing, in the interval before William bore her off to Mount Comeragh Lodge, to learn more of the mysterious Mr. Denny.

The thought of seeing him again made her throw back the bedclothes and slip down from the big bed. Clutching her borrowed nightgown about her, for it was far too large, she padded on bare feet to one of the windows and looked out. She found herself gazing onto a neat garden with clipped yew hedges and scythed lawns running down to a dark lake. At the far side of the lake, however, all traces of neatness and civilization vanished. The rolling hillside fell away into a deep trough, rearing up again steeply on the far side. Clouds chased one another in the wide, pale blue sky, and their changing fluffy shapes were reflected on the hillside beyond the lake, mottling the broad slopes, changing them from brown to green to purple like some moving patchwork.

Even as Kitty watched, the sunlight slid onto the lake and a glimmer grew gradually into a thousand points of light. The whole brooding surface of the water came to glittering life before her eyes. There were sounds of laughter from below her in the house—a clatter of metal and a burst of song.

Suddenly there came to Kitty the memory of another household, one that she had known as a child. She and her brother used to stay with their grandparents in Devon. It seemed so long ago, she had not given Pengelly a thought for years—but oh, the freedom of those days! She and her brother had run wild like gypsies, sticking fingers into bowls of cream in the dairy, sampling new-made jam in the still-room, riding the small half-wild ponies over the high, dark moors.

Her grandparents were long since dead, and Kitty had left childhood behind her when she married Johnny Harcombe. Strange that she should think of Pengelly after such an age, all because some maid below stairs had dropped a bucket or a coal scuttle. She felt an illogical lift of her spirits and sense of familiarity with the house. She wanted to explore.

CHAPTER FIVE

KITTY was not able to explore for some little while, for she had nothing to wear. Her sodden traveling clothes had been spirited away the night before, and though her boxes had come down the hill in the much-despised wheel-less wagon, it took time to get them brought up, and more time again for Martha to unpack.

As Martha bustled about the room, Kitty took stock of her surroundings. The bedroom was large enough, but a low ceiling and the old-fashioned but well-tended furnishings gave it a mellow air of comfort rather than elegance. The bed-hangings were faded almost white but were spotlessly clean, and the linen sheets had that silken softness which told of countless launderings.

Used as she was to changing the decoration and furniture in her own rooms whenever some new craze made last year's colors and shapes seem dowdy, Kitty could only suppose that the Denny family must be in straitened circumstances. All things Egyptian had been the mode last winter in London, and Kitty had been the first to sweep all her outmoded mahogany drawing-room furniture up into the attics and replace it by tables upheld by gilt sphinxes and all manner of objects which the London cabinetmakers fondly believed to have an Egyptian flavor. Kitty had been delighted and absorbed by this new flight of fancy, and had even designed a highly becoming fez which she wore on her golden curls; but like all fancies, she had grown weary of it, and it seemed to her now that the faded simplicity of her bedroom at Dennystown had much to recommend it.

She took care over choosing her dress. At first she rather favored a delectable figured muslin which would give her an air of fragile appeal, but finally she settled on a rather more severe walking gown, feeling that its elegance would provide the best contrast to her sodden and wind-blown state of the previous night. It was dark green, high-waisted and long-sleeved, the only trimming a narrow white ruffle at the neck and wrists. With her modishly short shining curls brushed back from her brow, her small feet shod in the daintiest of dark green kid slippers, Kitty was at length ready to face the world.

First she went to see Robert, but though he smiled wanly at his mama, there seemed no need for her to linger. The smell of wintergreen and other medicaments was overpowering, and so was the presence of both Miss Biddy and Martha. These two self-appointed nurses vied with each other in giving an account of Robert's symptoms, treating one another with wary neutrality and reserve which veiled their suspicion of each other. Kitty was only too relieved when

Miss Biddy suggested that she might like to go downstairs and partake of some refreshment with the rest of the family.

Declining Miss Biddy's offer to send a maid to escort her, Kitty went down the shallow stairs into the sunlit hall. Mick had been lying in wait for her for over an hour, and he came out of the morning room just as she reached the bottom step.

"Oh!" He executed a convincing start of surprise and hurried forward to take Kitty's hand and bow over it. "Lady Kitty—may I be permitted to call you that?—I am Mick Denny. My brother is gone to the stables, and he left instructions that I should make you welcome to Dennystown on behalf of all of us."

Kitty smiled up at the tall, exquisitely garbed young man. "You have certainly welcomed me more charmingly than Mr. Denny. How fortunate that he was called away. You have almost restored my confidence again."

Mick looked startled, but then grinned. "Oh, was Luke very churlish? You must not mind him. It is just his manner, you know."

"You relieve me," said Kitty rather dryly.

Mick looked as if he hardly knew how to take this; and evidently deciding that it was safest to take refuge behind his company manners, he said, "You must be in need of refreshment, ma'am. Will you step into the morning room and take a glass of something? I will send someone out to fetch my brother, and then we may partake of something to eat."

"Could we not go in search of Mr. Denny ourselves?" inquired Kitty, who was of no mind to be cooped up inside the house if there was an excuse to explore outside. "Indeed, I am not in the least hungry, and I would much rather be out in the fresh air on such a beautiful morning."

Mick was only too happy to usher the visitor out of the front door, and for a few minutes they stood together on the stone steps, enjoying the sunshine and the mild air while

Mick pointed out the hillside down which Kitty had ridden the night before. The distant rooftop of Father James's house was just visible above some trees at the far end of the lake.

As they stood there, Luke came through an ivy-covered archway. He was as carelessly dressed as ever, Kitty noticed, and there were two small shaggy dogs trotting at his heels. He bade Kitty a curt good morning. She looked with amusement from one brother to the other. They were both unusually tall and had the same dark hair and beaks of noses, but there the resemblance ended. Where Luke was carelessly dressed, Mick was precisely the opposite. His coat of dark blue superfine might have been molded to his form, the shoulders were modishly peaked so as to give him just the right degree of waisted elegance. His neckcloth was as high as that of any London dandy.

"Oh, there you are, Luke," exclaimed Mick. "Lady Kitty says that she is in no hurry to take any refreshment, and would much rather see the gardens and take a walk down to the side of the lake."

"I want to see everything!" declared Kitty in her sweet, drawling voice which somehow managed to give dramatic significance to the most commonplace remark. "I wish to visit the dairy, the stillroom, the stables and everything! I declare it must be an age since I was last in the country!"

Luke looked down at her. She thought his glance was more than a shade disparaging. He said, "You are nothing if not resilient, ma'am. But we have no neatly flagged paths for you to put your dainty feet on, you know. This is wild country up here, and if you don't want to soil your pretty shoes, you'll be wise to stay within doors."

"Nonsense! I am not such a ninny. Do you think I am afraid of a little mud, Mr. Denny? I was bred in the country."

"Oh, well," he said nonchalantly, "if you wish to play the part of a rural maiden for a day or two, it will serve to pass the time. I am told that your son will hardly be fit to be moved before then, and meanwhile Mick will be pleased to show you what Dennystown has to offer."

"He has already been most kind and welcoming. Most warmly welcoming."

He smiled in the tight-lipped, mocking way which had annoyed her so much at their first meeting and asked softly, "Are you complaining that my welcome lacked warmth?"

"Not at all," she replied in a voice as sweet as honey. "For your brother has explained it all to me. It is just your manner that is a trifle . . . farouche, Mr. Denny. I do not blame you for it in the least."

He laughed down at her, his dark eyes shining. "Your night's sleep has had a mellowing effect, I see."

"I am determined to be pleased with everything this morning, Mr. Denny. What do you mean to show me first? The stables?"

"I don't mean to show you anything. Mick is perfectly capable of doing that, and I daresay that if your Ladyship only smiles at him now and again, he'll be at your feet for as long as you want to keep him there."

"Luke!" Mick glared at his brother, but found his fiery glance ignored. "You are abominable! Take no notice of him, Lady Kitty!"

"Oh, I shall not. Never fear," she replied, holding onto her temper with difficulty. Her green eyes were bright with unuttered indignation, but her voice was still light and casual as she said, "I can see that you are determined to have the lowest opinion of me, sir. You are, of course, at liberty to think what you please."

He bowed gravely. "Thank you, ma'am."

"And if you wish to regard me as a frippery sort of female, and do not wish to waste your time showing me your possessions, I shall be more than happy to go with your brother.

Pray don't let me keep you. I fear I have already taken up too much of your time."

"Yes," he agreed, abominably impervious to her ironic tone. He turned to Mick and added, "We'll eat now. You may entertain her Ladyship after that. I'll need to leave for Clonmel within the hour if I am to be back before dark." And just as Kitty was struggling to find something to say that would express just what she thought of his manners while at the same time showing him how little she cared what he said or did, he turned to her and said, "I mean to call in at Mount Comeragh Lodge on my way home, ma'am. Do you wish to write a letter to Fossick, or will it suffice for me just to tell him that you are here and are anxious to see him?"

She blinked at him and said a little stiffly, "You are very good, sir. I do not think there will be any need for me to write to Sir William, however, for I have already done so. He will come and collect me at once, I daresay, so you will be quit of me almost immediately."

"You mean to leave your little boy with us, then?"

She had momentarily forgotten that Robert was too ill to travel. She said irritably, "How you delight in misunderstanding me, Mr. Denny. Of course I would not leave without Robert. But you will find that he will be quick to recover. Indeed, he did not look so very ill this morning . . . " At his look of surprise, she said in a nettled tone, "You do not believe me? I assure you, Robert is never ill for long."

"A most accommodating child," commented Luke dryly. "Well, am I just required to inform Fossick that you are here, ma'am?"

"If you please. Rest assured, Mr. Denny, that I shall not impose upon your hospitality one moment longer than is necessary."

He made no reply to this, merely glanced down at her in a somewhat derisive manner. Then he turned and looked toward the door of the house whence came Miss Biddy, leading a dark little girl by the hand. "Ah, Aunt Biddy! We thought we'd better partake of some refreshment at once, and then Mick and Mary can show her Ladyship around the garden." He turned to Kitty. "This is my sister Mary, ma'am, all dressed up in her Sunday best for your benefit. Let us all go indoors again, shall we? I don't want to waste any more time."

As soon as they had eaten, Luke departed for Clonmel and Miss Biddy took herself off to supervise Robert's sickroom once again. This left Kitty in the company of Mick and Mary. At first there had been some constraint between the young people and their visitor, but Kitty exerted herself to be as charming as she knew how, and by the time she had been taken around the stables and admired Mary's shaggy little pony, they were thoroughly at ease. And then Mick suggested they take a turn down to the lakeside. The grass had been scythed quite short and they walked without speaking to the water's edge, their feet making hardly a sound.

As they came to the brink of the water, a rowing boat nosed its way out of the overhanging willows. At the oars was a shabbily dressed man with a broad-brimmed hat pulled down over his dark, unshaven countenance, and in the stern crouched the small red-headed boy whom Kitty had noticed the previous evening. Both occupants of the boat looked positively startled at the sudden appearance of Mick and his two companions. Of the two, perhaps the small boy looked the more dismayed.

"Shamus!" exclaimed Mick sharply. "You know you've no right to be here!" And then added in a frankly unfriendly tone, "And what the devil are you doing here, Cullen? Nothing good, I'll wager!"

"I wanted a word with yourself, Mister Mick," replied the

stranger. "I sent down a message to you the other day, asking you to come up to the Castle to see me . . . "

"I never had it," retorted Mick, sounding as though the message would hardly have been welcome anyway. "But why could you not have come to the house and asked for me as anyone else would do?"

"And how could I be doing that, Mister Mick, when Denny said he'd turn the dogs on me if I laid foot on Dennystown land again? Denny's a hard man, and that's a fact."

"He only warned you away last year when you were preaching sedition to the servants. He'd not be worried at anything you could do now. But he'll be angry enough when he hears that you brought young Shamus here, when he's been particularly ordered to stay with Father James." Turning to Shamus, he said severely, "I trust you'll be able to explain yourself, Shamus, for I'll not take on the task of defending you!"

Shamus had not moved from his crouching position in the boat, but he cast Mary a beseeching glance.

"Oh, Mick! You'll not tell Luke!" she protested. " 'Twas the greatest bad luck that you saw him (or that Lady Kitty saw him) for how was Shamus to know that we'd come round the corner just at that moment?"

"He should not have left Father James's house."

" 'Twas myself that persuaded him, Mister Mick," Cullen put in. "And I'd not wish to get the little lad in trouble with Denny. I've been in too much trouble with himself in my time."

"Oh, very well," said Mick, relenting. "Mary, take him back to where he belongs, will you? You can go by the lake path. And you," he added, as Shamus began to scramble nimbly onto the bank, "you had best stay where you were told to stay, or you'll catch it!"

As the two children vanished along the marshy path beside the lake, Cullen said, "He's grown into a strong little lad, that! And he's more the image of his mammy than ever!"

"I never knew Shamus's mother," replied Mick curiously.

"Never knew Katie Finn? Ah, she was a real little beauty, Mister Mick. All the lads were wild for her, for all her quiet, strange ways. And even when she came back from Dublin after all that time, and she had not a shred of reputation left to her; even then she held that red head of hers as high as ever and wouldn't look at any of them . . . "

Mick, belatedly remembering that Kitty was still standing just behind him on the bank, broke in to say with an embarrassed laugh, "Lady Kitty! What must you think of me? Here am I positively forgetting your presence, while Cullen and I talk of an ancient scandal."

"Oh, pray," protested Kitty, smiling, "pray do not mind me. I had thought the little boy must be your brother, and now I am all at sea. Whose child is he?"

The man in the boat chuckled. "That's what Katie Finn would never tell, ma'am. Though some said that the father was a lad called Kelagher."

"Kelagher?" exclaimed Mick. "That dolt? I'll not believe it!"

"Kelagher was the only man Katie was ever kind to. He was a bit simple, you see, ma'am, and she wouldn't let the other lads tease him."

"I'll not believe it," reiterated Mick. "Not that Kelagher hasn't been the center of all our thoughts these last few weeks. He's got clean away, they say! And I, for one, hope he's not recaptured, for that trial of his was the most infamous thing. Even if Kelagher had murdered Harry St. Dennis (and I doubt that he did, at that), the poor wretch had a right to a fair trial. I was there when he was sentenced; and with the jury looking like scared mice and the way the judge summed up the case, there was never a doubt that they'd find him anything but guilty. If they'd had Judge Moore to try him, instead of sending for that devil from Dublin, Kelagher would have stood a chance."

Cullen chuckled. "I see you've not lost your way of ranting against injustice, Mister Mick. You almost put me in mind of the old days. You made some fine speeches to the boys then, I remember."

"I have no wish to remember old times," returned Mick coldly. "And for that matter, I've no more time to stand here talking with you, Cullen. If you must see me, come along to Dennystown and ask for me in a proper fashion. Denny will not harm you if your business is on the right side of the law; and if it isn't, I have no wish to see you. Good day."

Mick took Kitty's arm and led her briskly up the sloping grass toward the house, and presently they heard the sound of the oars dipping and splashing away along the perimeter of the lake. Mick slowed down then and mopped his brow with a large linen handkerchief.

"If Luke hears about the kind of entertainment I have offered you," he said gloomily, "I think he'll skin me alive. What a mull I have made of it."

"I do not think your brother cares in the least what you show me—not so long as he doesn't have to trouble about me himself."

"He'd trouble about it if he knew you'd seen Shamus," said Mick, looking very perturbed. "I suppose it would be too much to ask your Ladyship to forget that you ever did lay eyes on him?"

Kitty did not speak for a moment. She had no intention of betraying Mick or the little boy to that tyrannical Mr. Denny, but she meant to find out more of what was going on.

Besides, it was ridiculous that the young Dennys should be so much in awe of their elder brother. It was not as if he were their father; and if anything was ever going to be done about Mr. Denny's shockingly overbearing character, she must first make young Mick see that it was foolish to be so easily downtrodden. "Tell me about that little boy," she beseeched him. "Was he really banished from the house on my account?"

Mick appeared to be in a quandary as to how to answer her.

"If you do not wish to take the responsibility of telling me," she began.

"Lady Kitty," cried Mick in an agonized tone, "I truly may not tell you without Luke's permission."

"Then I shall ask him myself."

"No, ma'am! You must not."

"Must not?" she echoed. "I shall ask Mr. Denny any questions that I please."

He said despairingly, "Very well, ma'am. I deserve it if you do, after all."

"Oh, never fear that I shall give you away," she assured him. "Mr. Denny will not know that you have anything to do with it."

"You do not know him, Lady Kitty. Sometimes I think he can see into my mind, particularly when I would rather he could not . . . " He encountered her skeptical, almost quizzical glance, and said rather hurriedly, "Please do not think I am in the habit of deceiving Luke, Lady Kitty. I am never willing to do so."

"I think Mr. Denny is luckier than he deserves. Do you think he appreciates your loyalty?"

"Appreciates?" Mick sounded mystified, as though such a thing had not occurred to him. "I suppose that he may do so, but in general he would expect me to . . . to . . . "

"To comply with his every whim without question? To

obey him blindly? Why are you so very much afraid of him, I wonder?"

Mick started to deny this. "Indeed, I do not obey him blindly in the least, ma'am! It is just that he usually knows best what is to be done."

"He has certainly trained you to think so," agreed Kitty with a small smile which was only very slightly disdainful. "No wonder you do not dare to tell me about that little boy."

He drew himself up, flushing darkly at the mockery in her tone. "I am not afraid to tell you! It is just that Luke does not like it to be known that Shamus is here. I do not know what it is that he fears, for he will not tell me, but there must be some reason why he is so careful that Shamus is not seen by strangers." He hesitated, and seemed, at length, to decide that it was safer to tell her more. "I do not know, Lady Kitty, why my brother fears for Shamus's safety. It must have something to do with the way his mother and his grandparents died. They were killed, all three of them, and their farm burned to the ground; Luke found Shamus hiding on the hillside above the farm, half dead with cold and fright. It seems that the farm hand, Kelagher, had fled up the hill when he heard the marauders coming, and mercifully, Shamus had followed him there . . . "

Kitty gazed at the young man in horror. "You cannot mean it?" And when he assured her curtly that it was perfectly true, she added soberly, "Well, I trust the rebels were caught and punished for it. Not that anything can make up to that little boy for what he has lost, or what he may have seen . . . "

"Rebels!" retorted Mick scornfully. "It was not the rebels, ma'am. The rebels were, in general, gentler than that. No, it was the military who killed Shamus's grandparents and his mother, in the name of law and order." Mick's grim expression and the irony with which he spoke made him look, for a moment, more like his brother. "The authorities, we were told, had been sent word that the Finns were hiding arms in their loft. An unlikely story, it was, for old Finn was a loyal and law-abiding man. But of course, by the time anyone began to inquire into the matter, all the evidence had been burned, and there was no one to tell Finn's side of the tale. They set fire to his house before he had a chance to tell it for himself, and then they covered him with burning pitch and chased him backwards and forwards until he was burned to death."

Mick looked down into Kitty's appalled, incredulous face and said savagely, "Not a nice way to die, ma'am, you will agree." He did not wait for her to say anything. The fire went out of his eyes and he said bleakly, "They were kinder to Shamus's mother and his grandmother. They merely shot them both and burned his grandparents' bodies in the general conflagration." He shrugged and added, "And as for Shamus, we do not know how much he saw that night, but from the way he acts at the sight of a soldier's red coat, we think he must have seen a good deal."

"And the farm hand?" demanded Kitty. "Did he not testify against these monsters?"

Mick did not speak for a moment or two. Only after Kitty repeated her question did he say, "Kelagher was in other trouble soon afterwards. He fled the country before anyone could ask him anything about it. So Shamus is the only one who might be able to tell the truth of the matter, and Luke will not have him questioned."

For once, Kitty did not feel inclined to query the rightness of Luke's decision. She was wholly preoccupied with digesting the dreadful story Mick had just told her. It hardly seemed credible, and yet she had heard many tales of the atrocious cruelties of the late uprising, atrocities which had by no means been perpetrated entirely by the rebels. She

(72)

said slowly, "Does Mr. Denny believe that Shamus is still in danger? Surely no one could blame a small boy for the crimes of his family, even if they had been guilty?"

"I really do not know, Lady Kitty," Mick assured her, sounding at a loss in his own turn, "for I was away at the time. Luke had sent me to Hamburg some months before, to study, so I know very little of what happened. I wish I had been there," he added wistfully, "and that I could have spoken with Kelagher. I just cannot bring myself to credit . . . " He broke off and said in a more matter-of-fact tone, "But whatever the reason, ma'am, Luke seems to be convinced that Shamus has enemies. It seems unlikely to me, for who in the world could wish the little boy ill? But Luke is so careful of him, and is forever sending him out of the way when we have company. He is not usually fearful, but where Shamus is concerned, you'd think he saw danger behind every tree."

"I can understand it, I think," said Kitty musingly, "but you do not need to fear that I shall betray his presence here. How should I do so, when I do not know a soul for hundreds of miles?"

He looked discomfited and said awkwardly, "You . . . you are acquainted with Sir William Fossick, ma'am."

She eyed him coolly and challengingly. "What if I am?"

He looked more miserably embarrassed than before, but said doggedly, "Pray do not take this amiss, Lady Kitty, but it really would be better if you did not mention . . . " He paused, and then said quickly and imploringly, "Please, Lady Kitty, would you be so kind as to undertake not to tell Sir William about Shamus? It would be above all things great if you would keep it from him."

She regarded him with displeasure. "Very well. I will not speak of the little boy to him, but why everybody here persists in thinking poor William a villain, I cannot understand. A more law-abiding man I trust I shall never see. I do not believe," she added accusingly, "that you know anything about the matter. You have just been told by Mr. Denny that William is not to his liking, and you take all your opinions from him. Would it not be more diverting to develop your likes and dislikes for yourself?"

Mick emitted a short bark of laughter. "No one has forbidden me to like Fossick. You were at the Castle last night, ma'am. You saw the damage that was done there. That used to be our home, and you would not expect us to have much liking for the man who reduced it to that state, would you?"

Kitty said incredulously, "William did that? I do not believe it!"

He shrugged. "Oh, Fossick tried to pin it on the tinkers; but for all that, he wanted to buy the place, and since Luke would not sell . . . "

"Were you living there at the time?"

"Well no," Mick conceded, as though he felt this somehow weakened his case for the prosecution, "but Luke had hopes that we might soon have retrenched enough to be able to do so. Of course, I do not mean to say that Fossick ransacked the Castle himself. Indeed, I believe he was careful to be miles away at the time; but Luke says . . . "

"Luke says. Luke says," she mimicked him. "Do you know, I have had nothing but Mr. Denny's opinions and sayings quoted at me since I first arrived in your house, and I have so far not been able to agree with a single one of them. I must see whether I cannot manage to show you that even your excellent brother may be mistaken on rare occasions."

CHAPTER SIX

THEY WERE FLOGGING a man in the stable yard of Sir William Fossick's house. Mount Comeragh Lodge was a sizable mansion, as befitted a gentleman of such consequence as the deputy sheriff, so Miss Fossick, cowering in a distant room, was not obliged to hear the blows that were being administered. But she could not dismiss the matter from her mind. The servants came and went with closed, expressionless faces, not quite meeting her eye when she spoke to them. Her sewing lay idle in her lap. It was really impossible to concentrate.

It was a relief, therefore, when she saw her brother come into the room. He was a large man, as fair as a Norse god, with an elegant air about him which contrasted with his bronzed and healthy complexion. Miss Fossick, who admired her brother almost as much as she feared him, thought him the most handsome man in the world. He was tall and held himself well, and his very blue eyes were piercing and alert.

"There are several letters for you, William," she said timidly. "I told Morrisey to put them in the book-room. I hope I did right," she added hastily, as he looked at her, frowning sharply. "I will send for them, if you wish . . . "

He seemed unable to focus his mind on what she was saying. The truth was that his interrogation of the man in the yard had not turned out as he had wished. "What? Letters?" he repeated. He moved toward the door, saying, "That fellow I was questioning knew something, I could swear to it. When I asked him if he'd ever had speech with Luke Denny or his brother, he shied like a nervous horse."

"Never say that Luke Denny's been plaguing you again, dear!"

He turned on her savagely. "If I could find some reason to search that outlandish estate of his, I'll wager there'd be evidence to prove him in league with the United men. The trouble is, the fellow has to be treated with care, particularly with this Union in the offing. He's a damned papist, but he's a great deal of influence . . . " He sighed. "Young Mick Denny was as guilty as hell last year, but that crafty devil of a brother got him out of the country before I could lay my hands on him. That's what is so irritating. Duffy has no judgment. The man was just about to speak, I swear it, and then Duffy gave him a couple more blows and he fainted."

Miss Fossick gave vent to a little moan of protest.

He looked down at her derisively. " 'Tis well I'm not as squeamish as you, Eliza. How else do you think we can keep law and order in the county?"

"But . . . to use any human being so . . . so brutally, William . . . "

(76)

"Ah! Don't judge their feelings by your own, Eliza. They're half savage, most of them, and think nothing of a blow or two. Why, they are forever scrapping and fighting among themselves. They like nothing better than a good mill, and the more blood the better."

She said meekly, "I daresay you are right, dear."

"Of course I'm right. Keep them in their place, that's what I say, and don't listen to the idiots who say that the Catholic rabble should be educated and allowed to vote. Give them full bellies and an authority that they can look up to, and they'll be happier than ever they'd be if they had their blessed Ireland for the Irish. They're like children, Eliza. Children need discipline, and are all the better for a firm hand."

On this impressive note, Sir William stalked out of the room; but Miss Fossick was not left for long in peace. Ten minutes later he was back, a letter in his hand and an expression on his handsome face which made Miss Fossick reach for her vinaigrette.

"Eliza, when did you last write to Kitty Harcombe?"

Miss Fossick swallowed nervously, and stammered out that it had been all of six weeks ago. "Of course, I have not written since . . . since Lord Comeragh spoke to you . . . I mean . . . "

Sir William said tautly, "You invited Kitty to come here, didn't you?" She nodded, unable to speak. "Well, she is coming. Look at that, Eliza!" He threw a piece of paper down upon his sister's lap and turned away as if he could not bear to look at her. "This is the one time when it will spell disaster for her to come here, and for all I know, she is on her way!"

He went to the window and gazed out if it, unseeingly. He knew very well that he was being unfair. It was not Eliza's fault. It was entirely his own doing that Kitty had decided to come to Ireland. Had he not begged her to do so time after time? It was only when Lord Comeragh had made his staggering proposal that he had ceased to pester Kitty with his attentions. She had only written twice in answer to his own copious outpourings. He had been on the way, perhaps, to admitting defeat when Lord Comeragh announced that he wanted him to marry his great-niece, Amelia Braxton, thus inheriting all the earl's unentailed property when the old man died.

One did not turn down a chance of becoming one of the wealthiest men in Ireland. Even Kitty Harcombe was no fair exchange for that. And now, here was a letter from Kitty announcing that she wanted above all things to visit him, just at a time when Miss Amelia Braxton and her formidable mother had arrived at Kilnabawn for the whole business to be announced.

He turned back to his sister, who was looking as if she had seen a ghost.

"I cannot understand Lady Katherine's conduct at all," she said in a scandalized tone. "Really, I cannot."

Sir William laughed suddenly and loudly. "Oh, I'd not expect you to do that, Eliza! Kitty's a law unto herself. But I shall have to stop her. How can I be sure to get a letter to her in time?" He drew himself up, saying that he'd just remembered that John Perry was leaving for London that very day. He'd give him the letter to deliver. It would be safer that way.

TWO HOURS LATER Sir William found himself bowling toward the town of Clonmel in his high yellow-wheeled curricle. Beside him sat a tall angular lady in a very large purple bonnet. She was Lady Braxton, Sir William's future mother-in-law.

"I am sorry to hear that Miss Amelia has the headache," said Sir William, all civil concern. "Is it very bad?"

"Well, if you must know," said Lady Braxton, in a brisk no-nonsense voice, "she is perfectly well. The truth of the matter is, I wanted to speak to you privately."

If Sir William felt a qualm of unease at this threatening preamble, he did not show it. He merely remarked that it was a pleasure to have an opportunity to drive out with her Ladyship.

"Well, so long as you do not overturn me, William, I daresay I shall share your pleasure," she returned. "I am glad we are to drive to Clonmel, at all events, for I doubt if this fancy carriage of yours can survive on any but the smoothest roads."

This was ground upon which Sir William felt wholly sure of himself, and he lost no time in telling Lady Braxton of all the time and trouble he had taken to see that his carriages were as near perfect as wheeled vehicles could be. He might have gone on for some time, had not Lady Braxton cut him short.

"Now, William, that's enough about that. I have been trying to speak to you without Uncle Comeragh at my elbow, and this may be my only opportunity. You will not mind if I am frank?"

His experience of Lord Comeragh had taught him that it did not pay to be meek with members of that family. He said bluntly, "Do you not approve of me as a husband for Miss Amelia?"

Lady Braxton seemed to debate with herself. "Amelia is young for her age, you know, and this new notion of haste which Uncle Comeragh has got into his head, and this ball which he is giving for her on Thursday, I confess I do not wholly like it . . ."

"No more do I, ma'am."

She turned her bonneted head to look at him keenly. "Oh? Why not? I should have thought it might have suited you."

"How could you say so? You must have forgotten that the reason for this haste, as you call it, is that Lord Comeragh is in ill health. The Dublin doctors may be mistaken, of course, but one has only to see him in the throes of one of his attacks to know that he is a sick man. He has had a great deal to distress him of late . . ."

"Oh, the abduction of Harry's murderer, you mean?" said Lady Braxton. "Well, that was tiresome, of course; but Uncle Comeragh assures me that you will soon be recapturing the Kelagher man . . ."

"Certainly," returned Sir William, flushing a little. He waited for her to make some reference to the manner of Kelagher's abduction, and when she did not, he said earnestly, "It is a matter of concern to me, Lady Braxton, to keep his Lordship in a tranquil frame of mind. That is why I have consented to this rather hasty alliance. He has been very good to me, you know, and I should give a deal to see him contented in his last years."

She was impressed by his manly style of speaking, and more than a little reassured. She had, until that moment, been at a loss to see what there was about William Fossick which had so taken Lord Comeragh's fancy. There was the question of the inheritance, of course. As it was not possible to prevent the hated Luke Denny from inheriting the title, Lord Comeragh was prepared to go to any lengths to make sure that he inherited very little else. But why he had chosen William Fossick to marry Amelia, it had not been easy to see.

However, strenuous inquiries into the deputy sheriff's character and antecedents had yielded nothing more objectionable than the mild scandal of his flirtation with Kitty

Harcombe; and since she had been assured that he had relinquished all interest in that rather rakish widow, Lady Braxton thought that Amelia might fare worse for a husband. William Fossick might be ponderous, but she did not think her good little Amelia would mind that. And she could see that he was genuinely attached to Lord Comeragh. She was not at all fond of the earl herself, but she felt it only proper that William Fossick should regard his benefactor so warmly.

"But is there any need to be in such haste?" she demanded. "I should be happier if Uncle Comeragh could be prevailed upon not to announce your betrothal at the ball. After all, Amelia is only this instant come out of her seminary in Bath. She should have a chance, first, to find her feet in society."

Sir William made a noncommittal noise in his throat. He did not tell Lady Braxton that Amelia was lucky not to have been dragged off to a parson and married as soon as she arrived in Ireland. The old man seldom extended or accepted hospitality from his neighbors. If he wanted to see them, he sent for them. If he did not, then he refused to do so. It had taken Sir William some considerable effort to persuade Lord Comeragh that a betrothal party of some kind was a necessity. It would give rise to vulgar gossip, he said, if the wedding was hustled through. Lord Comeragh had agreed reluctantly, but it would not do to press him for further concessions.

He said carefully, "His Lordship is desperately anxious to bring this marriage about, you know."

"Good heavens, of course I know! He has talked of nothing else since we arrived."

"His Lordship's desire," said Sir William earnestly, "is to make sure that his inheritance does not fall into the wrong hands. You did not see him, did you, after Harry was murdered? I almost feared for his reason. But it was evident, when he came to himself, that he was not grieving over Harry's death so much as over the loss of his heir."

"Harry used to say," said Lady Braxton soberly, "that his grandfather did not value him as a person at all, only as the heir. I used to chide him for being foolish, but perhaps he was in the right of it."

Sir William turned his head and looked at Lady Braxton in cold surprise. "Harry never lacked for anything as far as I'm aware—unless it was discipline. The old man indulged him in everything. I do not mean to speak ill of him, Lady Braxton. Indeed, I was fond of Harry despite his wild ways. But he had no cause to feel ill-used."

"Oh, for my part," said Lady Braxton briskly, "I used to tell Harry that I was unable to feel truly sorry for anyone with an allowance of twenty thousand pounds a year . . ."

"That's it," said Sir William with energy. "Harry had everything, or he could have had everything if only he had been a little conciliating."

"By marrying that Beresford child, you mean?"

"Certainly, ma'am. Or any other respectable Protestant female in the land. So long as he married her and gave the family an heir, he could have done anything else he wanted. But instead, the pigheaded young fool chose to stay in the army against his grandfather's wishes."

"Uncle Comeragh was always in a fret that he would get killed in the war."

"Instead of which," said Sir William bitterly, "he was killed almost as soon as he came back from the war. When he came back to Kilnabawn he behaved in the most reckless fashion. He drank and sulked in his room for most of the days, and stole out every night to go drinking with his low companions in the town."

"He must have been in some trouble," said Lady Braxton

in a musing tone. "He was never one to be in the sullens for long. What was it, William? Have you any notion?"

Sir William shrugged his elegant shoulders. "God knows. Some maggot that he had got into that red head of his, I daresay. He had been drinking more than was good for him. He was seen leaving an alehouse, arguing with that Kelagher creature on the very night that he was murdered."

He fell silent, and the only sound was the rumble of wheels and the clip-clop of the horses upon the roadway. At length Sir William said, rather defensively, "We were occupied with other things at the time. The rebellion was brewing, you know, and the rebels were hiding arms in the hill cabins, and the United agents seemed to be everywhere. I simply did not give much time to Harry's megrims, ma'am, and believe me, I have regretted it ever since the morning when we found him dead upon the hillside."

CHAPTER SEVEN

SIR WILLIAM drove his team with the same confident dexterity with which he handled all his affairs. Lady Braxton could not help admiring him for it. They bowled along the road so smoothly and speedily that it seemed almost no time before the rooftops of the town and the delicate octagonal tower of St. Mary's Church came into view against the spectacular backdrop of green fields and distant purple hills. The sky was blue and wide, feathered with white clouds. The little town lay snugly in its valley beside the shining river, looking so peaceful and calm that it seemed a wonder that the ugly events of the rebellion and Harry's murder could ever have taken place in this placid part of Ireland.

As they came into the first poor streets the way became

crowded with donkey carts, stray dogs, and grubby-faced children. Sir William maneuvered his way through these hazards without appreciably slackening his pace. A pony and trap shot out suddenly from a side road, but they evaded it with scarcely a check. In the hurly-burly of handcarts, pedestrians, sheep, and numerous cats and dogs, Lady Braxton would have felt happier if they had slowed down to a walk. Plainly, however, this man whom Amelia was going to marry was perfectly at ease driving in these impossible conditions.

She resisted the temptation to clutch at the side of the curricle with her gloved hands, and began to look about her with interest as they passed under the archway which led to the smarter part of the town.

Here Sir William did slacken his pace in order to make it easier to point out the architectural improvements which had been effected since Lady Braxton's last visit, and so that he might acknowledge the greetings of various persons who were to be seen at intervals along the way. At the sight of the well-known curricle, hats were doffed and curtsies dropped by women at the doorways of their shops.

He inclined his head in answer to some of the bows and greetings, but he showed no inclination to stop and converse with anyone.

He told his passenger who some of the more interesting personages were, however, adding cheerfully, "But you will have to apply to my sister Eliza for all the latest on-dits, Lady Braxton. She is always marvelously well informed on all that is going forward. Next time there is a fine day, and it is convenient to yourself, I suggest that I drive you out in my barouche. That way I shall have an opportunity of getting better acquainted with Miss Amelia, and you and Eliza can have a comfortable coze together. Eliza always tells me that I am distressingly lacking in knowledge when it comes to knowing about the latest gowns and bonnets, and in noticing who has danced twice with some female or other."

Lady Braxton said that she would be quite pleased to drive out with him in this way, adding rather more in character, "Though I cannot see how it will be of the slightest interest to me to know about the local scandals, my dear William. I hardly know a single soul in the neighborhood. There is nobody here with whom I can claim more than the most distant acquaintance, except . . ." She broke off suddenly to say severely, "But we were discussing Amelia. I must try to make you understand why I am concerned about her. She is an innocent, rather timid child. You will have seen that for yourself, and if you contrive to win her affection, I believe she will make you a good wife. But at the moment she is quite overset by the sudden transition between the schoolroom and the prospect of becoming a married woman, and is somewhat appalled at the prospect of being sent away from home.

"Of course, I have striven to explain the advantages, to make her see that she will become not only Lady Fossick, but also a great and wealthy lady in her own right. But Amelia is not worldly, you know. Perhaps it is my fault that she is unaware of the benefits and advantages of wealth and worldly consequence.

"I do not know if you are aware of it, William, but my father was a somewhat improvident man, too fond of the gaming tables by far, and my sister and I were constantly aware, in our young days, of the state of his fortunes. One day we would be affluent, with our own carriages and servants. The next it would be very much the reverse and we girls would be sent to stay with more well-to-do relatives until Papa had a run of good luck again.

"From the day I married poor Braxton, of course, it has been very different for me, and I have always been determined that my daughters should not be brought up in such a sadly rackety fashion."

Sir William cleared his throat in a somewhat embarrassed way, preparing to say something, but she forestalled him. "So my poor Amelia views the prospect of her good fortune as more alarming than anything else. William, only be a little gentle and easy with her at first, and I am convinced that you will not regret it! Now that I have had a chance to speak with you, I feel that I shall be doing the best for Amelia by agreeing to Uncle Comeragh's plan. Indeed, I should be very foolish if I refused it. But so much will depend upon whether Amelia is given a chance to become a little acquainted with you before she is led to the altar."

Sir William said coldy, "Believe me, Lady Braxton, I am as much aware of the need for caution as you are. I am conscious that Miss Amelia regards me with the liveliest dread . . ."

"Not dread!" she protested. "She merely holds you in awe, which is not at all the same thing. I daresay that once again I am to blame, for I have been so concerned to point out your good qualities: your bravery in the late rebellion, your intelligence, the esteem in which Uncle Comeragh holds you. She is quite overcome by your consequence."

Sir William, who had an excellent opinion of his own consequence also, appeared to be mollified. "Well, ma'am," he said cheerfully, "do not worry your head about it. I shall endeavor to get to know Miss Amelia better, and to give her a chance to know me. You need not think, whatever his Lordship's wishes may be, that I shall try to terrorize her into accepting my advances before she is ready to receive them. As you may know," he added, once more deeming boldness to be the best approach to Lady Braxton's good graces, "I am not without a little experience with females, and I hope you

(87)

will not think me a coxcomb if I tell you that I have had some degree of success with the fair sex. Give me a little time, and you shall see for yourself."

"Give Amelia a little time, and I do not doubt it," retorted Lady Braxton. "It may comfort you to know that she finds you very good-looking." She eyed him a trifle severely, and frankness being more natural to her than restraint, added, "No doubt Kitty Harcombe also admired your good looks, William?"

Sir William did not reply.

She said relentlessly, "Well, Kitty Harcombe knows a good deal about the world, and about men; and Amelia knows nothing at all. Nor is she adept at looking after her own interests."

"When Amelia is married to me," returned the deputy sheriff, refusing to be daunted, "she will not need to know how to look after her interests. I shall be quite able to do that, ma'am. I have no liking for the sort of forceful modern female who thinks she must take all the reins of the household into her hands."

Lady Braxton chuckled, inwardly acknowledging a feeling of admiration for his resolution in the face of her attack. "And yet you were one of Kitty Harcombe's court? If Kitty is not a modern forceful female, I do not know who is!"

This was plain speaking, indeed; but if Sir William did not much relish it, there was no sign of any emotion on his fair, firm-lipped face. He turned his head and gave Lady Braxton a sharp look. "As you must know, ma'am, I have already given Lord Comeragh my word that I am done with Lady Kitty," and then, as the recollection of Kitty's letter struck him like an inward blow, he added with vehemence, "Absolutely finished with her! She was just an episode. No more."

"I'm very glad to hear it," returned Lady Braxton, and

then exclaimed suddenly, "Good gracious! Who is that? It looks like my Cousin Luke."

Luke Denny and an elderly gentleman were riding slowly toward them. Luke was hatless, and looked preoccupied as he listened to whatever Judge Moore was saying to him. Sir William thought that Luke presented a very countrified and ordinary appearance in his shabby brown coat and buckskins: Lady Braxton would not be favorably impressed by her distant cousin. He got ready to bow coldly in passing to the pair (he could always excuse himself later to Judge Moore, who knew perfectly well how it was between Luke Denny and himself), but Luke looked up at that moment, saw Lady Braxton, and spurred his horse forward. "Good God, Euphemia!" he exclaimed. "What in the world are you doing here?" He nodded briefly to Sir William, and then seeming to recollect something, added, "Oh, so you are staying at Kilnabawn, are you, Euphemia?"

Lady Braxton nodded. "It is an age since I have seen you, Luke. I did not expect even to know you by sight. But you have not changed one whit, I declare."

He eyed her and said dryly, "I'll tell you if you have changed when I have seen you without that fearful bonnet. Do not tell me that it is all the crack in London, for I'll not believe it!"

"Really, Denny!" protested Sir William.

Lady Braxton said indulgently, "Evidently your manners are much the same as ever, Cousin. But for your information, I have had this particular hat these two seasons. As a widow with a grown-up daughter, I do not need to concern myself with looking modish any more."

She glanced toward Luke's elderly companion, who was hanging back a little during this interchange, and added, holding out her hand, "How do you do, Judge Moore! Since my cousin never had any manners, and since Sir William appears to have forgotten his, we had best make ourselves known to each other, do you not think?"

Luke laughed softly and Sir William began to make some sort of apology, but Judge Moore came forward and said easily that he remembered Lady Braxton perfectly well and was very happy to see her in County Tipperary, and had, moreover, received an invitation to a ball at Kilnabawn. He also inquired after Lord Comeragh's health, which he said had been causing all the county a vast deal of concern.

"Oh, he is in very good spirits, all things considered," replied Lady Braxton. "But, of course, he is of a great age; we are none of us as young as we should like to be. But he is set on giving this party, you know."

"Anyone would think you were nearing your dotage, Euphemia," remarked Luke. "Whereas I happen to know that you are not more than four years older than myself."

"Four and a half years precisely," she corrected him, smiling. "Oh, what marvelous carefree days those were when we all stayed together at the Castle!" She turned to Sir William, who had been listening to this exchange with an expression of stiff disapproval on his face, and said, "You must know, William, that whenever my late papa was in bad odor with Uncle Comeragh because of his gaming propensities, we used to be sent to Mount Comeragh Castle until the storm had blown over. Once we stayed there as much as a whole year. I daresay poor papa must have been in dire financial straits, but I do not remember about that. I do recall, however, that those times were among the happiest in my childhood."

"Indeed," said Sir William in a colorless tone.

"Well, now that your are here," said Judge Moore cheerfully, "you must stay some time so that we may return his Lordship's hospitality in form. Even if his Lordship is not in the best of health, he will surely spare you to us for a day. I shall never be forgiven by Maria if I do not succeed in getting you to come over to Knocklong, Lady Braxton."

"Oh, and you must pay us a visit at Dennystown, too," put in Luke, smiling at her. "I'd wait upon you at Kilnabawn if I did not think it would give the old man an apoplexy to see me there." He saw the doubtful look dawning upon Lady Braxton's high-nosed countenance, and added, "Come, Euphemia! Do not tell me that an aging widow with a grown-up daughter like yourself cannot summon the courage to go wherever she wants."

"Now, Denny," said Sir William, rather loudly, "if her Ladyship is staying with Lord Comeragh, she will feel herself obliged to consider his wishes."

Luke turned his head and said coolly, "Well, it is well known that you have always studied Lord Comeragh's wishes, Fossick—almost made a life study of them, haven't you? But why should Euphemia do so?"

"You will grant," returned the deputy sheriff, flushed but dogged, "you will grant that Lady Braxton has a perfect right to decline your invitation if she wishes?"

"Oh, certainly, Do you wish to decline it, Euphemia?"

"I don't know," she returned in her accustomed blunt style. "I don't wish to, of course . . ."

"While we are on the subject of invitations, Fossick," said Luke, blandly ignoring Lady Braxton's evident hesitation, "I was meaning to call by at Mount Comeragh Lodge on my way home, but I have thought of something better. Judge Moore and some others are coming up to Dennystown to-morrow to shoot snipe and to flight the duck. They will stay the night and we shall be in place for the dawn flight the next morning. If the notice is not too short for you, Fossick, why not join us?"

"A capital plan, Fossick," interjoined the judge, who

knew full well that the deputy sheriff and Luke had been less than friendly for some time, and thought it an excellent plan that they should bury their grievance in this way. "Do join us."

It was Sir William's turn to hesitate. "I hardly think . . ." he began, but since he had been puzzling in his mind for some days how he might gain access to Dennystown without causing undue comment, his natural inclination to refuse Luke's invitation was immediately at war with his baser instincts. Fortunately for him, Lady Braxton had by now recovered herself.

"Thank you, Luke. I fear that I shall not be able to visit you at Dennystown. William! Have the goodness to drive on. Amelia will be wondering what has become of us."

"Amelia?" murmured Luke. "Is she the daughter of whom you were boasting? Surely she cannot be long out of the nursery?"

"On the contrary, Cousin," she replied, "Amelia is of an age to be married," and as Luke raised his brows at this statement, she added for good measure, "And, indeed, it was to arrange Amelia's betrothal that we are come into Ireland, so you will understand that there will not be much time for jauntering about the countryside."

Luke's dark eyes narrowed. Then he said lightly, "Oh, naturally the business of becoming a mama-in-law will take up a good deal of your strength. May I ask, who is the lucky man? Do not tell me, Fossick, that it is yourself?"

"It is." Sir William did not at all relish this conversation, but since both Luke and Judge Moore had turned their horses and were riding one on each side of the curricle, there did not seem to be any obvious way of bringing it to an end.

"What an enterprising fellow you are, to be sure," remarked Luke. "I had no notion until the last twenty-four hours that you were such a man for the ladies, Fossick. I had always entertained the idea that your prowess was more in the . . . er . . . military line. That is what I so like in you, Fossick. You never fail to surprise me."

"You have the advantage of me, Denny," returned the deputy sheriff, "for I have not the least idea of your meaning."

"No?" Luke did not seem to be in any haste to enlighten his victim. Instead, he broke in upon the quietly spoken conversation which had meanwhile been going on between Lady Braxton and Judge Moore, and said, "I suppose I must now bid you goodbye, Euphemia. We have company at Dennystown at present, and if I do not go home and play the polite host, Aunt Biddy will give me a trimming."

"Is Aunt Biddy still as great a dragon as ever? How she used to scold us when we got our clothes dirty!"

"She is just the same," he assured her, smiling.

She smiled back at him. "You understand, do you not, why I cannot come to Dennystown."

"I understand perfectly," he replied, glancing momentarily at the deputy sheriff. "Is your Amelia's betrothal to be announced very soon?"

"I believe so. I do not know if it will be announced at Thursday's ball, but Uncle Comeragh wishes it to be soon. He has been kind enough to take an interest in the child, you see . . ." She paused, recollecting that the reason for Lord Comeragh's interest was in reality to keep Luke out of what he might regard as his rightful inheritance. However, she decided that he had not noticed anything amiss, for he did not pursue the subject.

He turned, instead, to Sir William and said, "Well, Fossick, do you mean to join us tomorrow? We can show you some good sport, I believe, and we can discuss that other matter at the same time."

"I cannot imagine, Denny," returned Sir William coldly, "that you and I can have anything profitable to discuss."

"Oh, come, Fossick," put in Judge Moore persuasively, "we are all going: Pennefather, young Captain Dillon, and myself. 'Twill be a capital day's sport, of that I am certain."

"No doubt," returned Sir William with scant enthusiasm, "but unfortunately I have a great deal to do this week, and can ill spare the time."

Luke's narrowed eyes swept from the deputy sheriff to Lady Braxton and back again. "Ah," he murmured. "No doubt, with the prospect of becoming a married man, you will feel the need to set your affairs in order?"

"Quite," snapped Sir William.

"In which case," said Luke slowly, "in which case, I really do not think you should lose any time before coming to Dennystown. Whether you wish to shoot the duck, or not, is for you to decide, but I should perhaps have made it clear to you at the outset that the visitors at Dennystown are only there by mistake. The lady is on her way to visit you, Fossick, and I do not think she has the least inkling that you are about to enter into a state of matrimony with Euphemia's child."

Sir William shot a startled glance at his tormentor's darkly mocking countenance. He felt, rather than saw, Lady Braxton's interested gaze upon him. He managed to answer with an attempt at airiness, however. "But why should anyone know that I was about to become betrothed? I did not know it myself until a short while ago."

Lady Braxton, who could not help but see that Luke was enjoying himself at Sir William's expense, and that Sir William was not enjoying the jest at all, said roundly, "My dear Luke! Pray remember that I, for one, am far too well aware of your horrid teasing ways to credit anything you may say. So do not try to hint that some specter from Sir William's past is lurking up at Dennystown . . ."

Luke's smile deepened. "Not a specter, precisely . . ."

Judge Moore broke in jovially, "Do not tell us, Denny, that you have no lovely ladies for us at Dennystown after all! Why, you'll be lucky if George Dillon doesn't call you out if he's disappointed. He's changed around all his duties for the week, he told me. He wasn't going to let anything prevent him from being one of the first to fix his interest with the famous Lady Kitty Harcombe."

There was a pause. Luke said lightly, "I shall never cease to be amazed at the speed with which news gets about in the county. No wonder George was available all of a sudden." He lifted his head and met the deputy sheriff's startled, incredulous, but horrified gaze. He said gently, "Yes, Fossick. It is unbelievable, I know, but her Ladyship is indeed at Dennystown. I think you would be wise, therefore, to take George Dillon for an example and make a push to come and see her."

Sir William did not speak.

Lady Braxton, however, said coldly and clearly, "I agree. You should definitely go to Dennystown and see her Ladyship, Sir William! I do not feel that there is any time to be lost."

CHAPTER EIGHT

WHEN SIR WILLIAM CAME BACK to Mount Comeragh Lodge late that evening, he felt weary to his very bones. Lady Braxton had left him in no doubt as to her meaning: Kitty Harcombe was to be removed, or she and Amelia would depart for England themselves. If Kitty remained, the marriage would be out of the question.

Sir William had accepted her ultimatum. He had no choice in the matter, and at least he could console himself that Lady Braxton had agreed to keep the matter from Lord Comeragh for the time being. She told him that she feared to upset the earl in his present precarious state of health, but Sir William suspected that Lady Braxton was, in fact, reluctant to make any move which might forever ruin her daughter's chances of making a brilliant match. This gave Sir William a warm and comforting sense of power. He would win through. He was sure of it.

"William, dear," said Miss Fossick timidly at his side, "there is a man waiting to see you. I told them to put him in the gun-room, dear. Do you wish to speak with him directly?"

It was dark in the gun-room, and it was a moment before Sir William could be sure that the man sitting there was the one he had been expecting.

"So you came at last. I expected you this morning," he said as he locked the door.

"I came as soon as I could, sir."

"Well? What have you to tell me?"

"What you was after wanting to know," replied the other. "I have just come from Dennystown."

"Dennystown?" echoed the deputy sheriff, his blue eyes very cold and alert. "And what of that?"

"You wanted me to find the Green Man, did you not, sir?"

Sir William said brusquely, "If you know who he is, Cullen, tell me. You'll do yourself no good by all this talk."

"Very well, sir. The Green Man is Mick Denny."

"Mick? Mick Denny?" reiterated the deputy sheriff, as though he could hardly believe he had heard aright. "Good God!" he added, after a pause. "But it's possible . . . it's possible."

"It's certain," retorted the other with a note of undisguised satisfaction in his voice. "I had a notion of it from something I found up at the Castle, and now I've spoken with Mister Mick, I'm sure of it."

Sir William was almost beyond speech for a moment. If this were true, if Cullen had really hit upon the true identity of his tormentor, then it would be worth paying every penny of the exorbitant sum he demanded. It had gone against the grain to employ Cullen, for the man was not only a rogue, but had also been one of the minor thorns in the deputy sheriff's side during the days of the Rebellion. But Sir William would have done anything to bring down the Green Man. And it really looked as if his gamble had paid off.

But he had to be sure. "How could it be young Denny?" he demanded sharply. "He was abroad until just after Christmas. Everybody knows that Denny hustled him out of the country last spring, just in time to avoid his being arrested as a troublemaker. He would have been away at the time when the Green Man was most active."

" 'Tis my belief," Cullen said, "that he was living at the Castle all the while. 'Twas just by chance, sir, that I went there two nights ago. I was after needing a place to sleep, not having the price of a bed as I had last evening, thanks to your honor's generosity . . ." He paused, making the deputy sheriff a little bow.

"Get on, man!"

"Well, I went to the Castle, sir, it being empty. And when I got there I was searching about for a good place to bed down, when I was put in mind of something young Mister Mick had shown me in the old days. 'Tis a secret room, sir, behind the altar in the chapel. Mister Mick took me there one time and showed me the way into it. There's a carved screen behind the altar: some class of a screen with our Lord and the loaves and the fishes. You pull at one of the fish's heads, sir, and 'tis the handle of a door into the room behind. Mister Mick was after telling me that the priests used to live there in the days of the old penal laws, and he said that if ever I needed somewhere to hide . . ."

"A priest's hole," breathed Sir William. "I might have known there would be such a thing at the Castle."

" 'Tis a deal better than a hole, sir," Cullen objected, being of a literal turn of mind. " 'Tis a quite large room, with a passage out of it that takes you out onto the hillside. A man could live there for years if he had a mind to."

"And you think young Denny was there all the time? By God!" Sir William cried explosively as the audacity of the thing dawned fully upon his understanding. "It might well be so! But I'll need proof, proof up to the very hilt before I can bring young Denny in, you know. If I lay a finger on him before I have unshakable evidence of his guilt, I'll have a hornet's nest around my ears. That smooth devil Denny has strings to pull in the most unlikely places. God knows how he manages it, but he does. But, by heaven, if I can prove that his young brother is no better than a common felon, I'll lay Denny'll sing a different tune!"

"That room is proof enough to my mind, sir. I had all night to look about me, you see, and I'll lay you any odds you like that Kelagher had been hiding there until very recently. There was a bed there that had obviously been slept in, and I found this . . ." Cullen began to grope in his leather duffel bag, and he pulled out a bedraggled object which he handed to the deputy sheriff.

Sir William studied it for a moment. Then he laid it down upon the table and said in a voice of quiet triumph, "Yes. It is the hangman's mask, all right. What else did you find?"

Cullen said regretfully, "Nothing else that you could actually call proof, sir; but if that priest's room has not been lived in, and lived in regular for a deal of time, I'm no judge of anything. Besides, 'tis well known that Mick Denny does not wish you well, your honor."

"He'll have less cause to wish me well if what you say is true," said William savagely. "And that damned superior brother of his! Of course, I should have seen it all along. The whole business has been aimed at myself from the beginning, only I hadn't the wit to see it. Why, one out of every two of the wretches whom the Green Man has taken away has been

(99)

a Dennystown dependent, or in some way connected with them. There was Old Mrs. Tomey, and that young fellow from the forge, and now Kelagher . . ."

" 'Tis easier for an outsider to see these things, sir," said Cullen soothingly. "And I've ways of knowing things, your honor, which you could not have."

"Take care that I do not ask what they are, Cullen! I could very well do so, you know."

"So you could," returned the other with exasperating equanimity, "but you'd not expect me to be after telling you, would you now?"

Sir Willam's blue eyes narrowed. "You could be made to tell."

"That's as may be, sir, but with a weak heart like mine, 'tis more than likely I'd be dead before your honor made any discoveries. Besides, 'tis a well-known fact, sir, that the way to unlock Matt Cullen's secrets is with gold. Guineas are powerful persuaders, and that's a fact."

"You have had a deal of gold from me already," replied Sir William contemptuously. "And you'll get more, as I promised you, when the Green Man's been taken, dead or alive." It occurred to the deputy sheriff, all of a sudden, that if the Green Man happened to be killed resisting arrest, it would not be altogether a bad thing. There would be no tedious trial with the chance for every hothead and romantic for miles to make a hero of him. "Dead or alive," he repeated deliberately. "It matters little which."

"But I understood," said Cullen, looking aggrieved, "that it was just the name of the Green Man you were after needing?"

"You must know that this is very different from what I expected," said Sir William in the tone of one who intends to stand no nonsense. "If it had been a farmer's son, or some person in a small way of trade in the town, I could have

(100)

brought him in and forced a confession from him, but Mick
Denny is another matter . . . In fact, I must contrive, somehow, to catch him red-handed. It should be possible."

"Something in the nature of a trap, sir?" suggested Cullen
gently.

"Mm. But how best to bait it? I must have time to think
about this. The devil of it is that I'm pledged to sleep at
Dennystown tomorrow night. I've some business there to
settle," he said vaguely. Indeed, the business of Kitty and
how best to dispatch her back to England had faded into the
background of his thoughts. He had decided, earlier, that
there was nothing for it but to tell Kitty the true state of
affairs and to send her to Dublin in his own coach. Still, Kitty
and her ill-timed gyrations were small beer compared with
the chance of capturing his enemy at last.

"Yes," he repeated slowly, "we must think how best to set
the trap . . ."

"I've an idea as to how it could be done, sir."

"Well?"

"You know John Lenehan, sir? Him that you've taken into
the jail?"

Sir William nodded. "What of him?"

"He used to be a friend of young Mick Denny's. A friend
from the old days, that is. If I were to go to Mister Mick and
let drop, like, that poor John was in trouble with your honor,
and like to be flogged, I'll wager that Mister Mick would be
powerful indignant about it. Powerful indignant. And I'll
wager he'd do his best to see that John was not left in the
jail . . ."

Cullen glanced slyly at the deputy sheriff to see how his
suggestion was being received, but only Sir William's blue
eyes, narrowed and very intent, gave any inkling of the fire
within. A dangerous man, Sir William. For all his blustering
and loud-laughing ways, he had a singleness of purpose

which carried him unswervingly forward to whatever goal he had in view. People who opposed him, and in these days there were not many, did not prosper.

To Cullen's knowledge (and he prided himself that he knew a great deal more about the deputy sheriff than most), there were only two people who had ever completely defeated William Fossick. One had been Luke Denny. The other had been a mere slip of a girl whom William Fossick had been mad for, and who would not have him. Well, poor Katie Finn might have been better to have become the deputy sheriff's mistress than to have stayed home and died of a yeoman's bullet. Cullen wondered briefly if Sir William might have had anything to do with the burning of the Finn farmstead. Rumor had laid that particular crime at the door of the high sheriff, Mr. Thomas Judkin-Fitzgerald, but Cullen, who was, after all, one of the most talented rumor-mongers in the county, had a proper contempt for such things.

He saw Sir William watching him, waiting for him to continue, so he said, "I could see Mister Mick, sir, and say that John Lenehan's to be tortured. It's my guess that he'll try to get him out before that happens."

"Ah," murmured Sir William, rubbing his well-manicured hands together. "And then we shall see what we shall see . . ."

After another moment he returned to his normal, businesslike manner. "We must plan this carefully," he said. "I shall go to Dennystown tomorrow, as I have been bidden to do. Part of my business is to arrange for a certain English lady to be escorted to Dublin, so I shall arrive there earlier than the other gentlemen, for there'll be details to discuss. Do you think you could arrange for young Mick to fall into our trap while I am yet at Dennystown?"

"I could that, sir. I'll tell Mister Mick that John Lenehan's to be tortured on Thursday morning. That should make certain of his trying to get him out on Wednesday night. And if you could contrive to have some of your men hidden up in the hills above Dennystown, between there and the town, like . . ."

"There will be no need to conceal them. I shall take them with me, but not for the purpose of capturing young Mick. We'll get young Mick in Clonmel, preferably in the act of freeing Lenehan."

He added, seeing that Cullen was looking puzzled, "I shall take a platoon of yeomanry up to Dennystown with me. I'm to give the English lady safe escort to Dublin, and as I can say with truth that I am too occupied here to escort her myself, it will not be thought odd in me to send her under a heavy guard. And then," he concluded, almost exultantly, "when we've got young Mick under lock and key, we'll take Dennystown to pieces. We"ll smoke them out of there like the rebel rats they are, and there'll be no time for Denny to go whining around the countryside trying to drum up sympathy and support."

) (CHAPTER NINE) ((

CULLEN WAYLAID MICK well out of sight of the Dennystown buildings. He had lain in wait for him since dawn, and he slipped out onto the pathway silently.

"Oh, it's you again, Cullen. You're nothing if not persistent. Well, if it's money you want, I'm afraid you're out of luck."

"It's not money . . ."

"What, then? You would not look so mysterious if it weren't something important."

There was a pause. Mick dismounted reluctantly and waited with exaggerated patience for the other man to say what he had to say.

Cullen spoke at last. "Can you find the Green Man for me, Mister Mick? I'm thinking you could if you wished to."

"The Green Man?" Mick's voice was sharp with astonishment. "The Green Man? What the devil do you want with the fellow? I hardly think he'd exert himself to help anyone as slippery and resourceful as yourself, Cullen. The Green Man is supposed to help only the helpless, you know; and whatever you may be, you're hardly that."

Cullen chuckled. Then he said, "You don't deny that the Green Man exists, do you?"

"Not after the Kelagher affair. How could I? But that's not to say that I know who he is."

"And not to say that you'd tell, even if you knew, eh, Mister Mick?"

Mick looked curiously at his companion. Matt Cullen looked seedier and more dissolute than when Mick had known him previously. "Well, what do you want with the Green Man, anyway?"

Cullen sighed and said abruptly, "You remember John Lenehan? Him that left the country so sudden when the troubles began?"

"Of course I remember him," returned Mick impatiently. "As you probably know, we left at much the same time."

"Well, the word was spread around that John had been saved by the Green Man . . ."

"Well, that's a lie, anyway."

"I don't know how these tales spread about, Mister Mick, but there's no stopping them once they get a hold. I saw John myself only this morning, and he swore black and blue that there was no truth in it, either."

"Well, then . . ."

"But you'd need to be able to do better than swear black and blue to make Sir William Fossick believe that

John is innocent. He's a powerful persistent man, is Sir William."

"What has Fossick to do with it? He can hardly be after John for his part in the Cahir raid, for since the Amnesty was declared, the men who were in that affair have been allowed back. Luke was saying so only the other day."

"I should have explained to you, Mister Mick," said the other solemnly, "John Lenehan was in the Clonmel jail when I saw him. He's in bad trouble."

"What has he done?"

"That's just it, Mister Mick! He's done nothing. But Sir William must have heard tell of this tale of the Green Man saving him last year, and he's got it into his head that John must know who the Green Man is. You know what Sir William is like once he gets a notion into his head."

"Even Fossick can hardly keep Lenehan imprisoned on the suspicion that he once saw the Green Man. There's nothing criminal about that. If there was, Fossick'd be the most guilty of all, for he was in close converse with him that day on Kilnabawn Bridge. Gad, but I wish I'd seen his face when the Green Man and Kelagher plunged into the water, or onto their raft, whichever it was! It must have been a sight!"

After a pause Cullen said, "Sir William is powerful anxious to have the Green Man at the end of a rope. You don't think he'd let go of a chance to question John Lenehan if he thought there was anything to be got from him, do you? As everyone knows, John goes into the town on Saturdays, and while he was away the deputy sheriff's men searched his house and found gunpowder stored under the floorboards, or so they said. John is not as young as he was, and he's mighty afraid of being hurt, Mister Mick. It's my belief that he'd tell Sir William anything he knew, and welcome, but he can't tell what he don't know. And the day after tomorrow, when he's had another couple of nights in the jail to think about it, Sir

William's given instructions that John's to be flogged. 'Tis wicked, that's what it is! Sir William'll have him killed, and all for nothing. That's why I thought, Mister Mick, that if the Green Man were to hear tell of John's trouble, he might try to get him out of there."

"Whereabouts in the jail is he?"

"Chained to the wall in the square tower. 'Twas there that I saw him last evening. All gray and shaking he was," Cullen added ghoulishly. "That's the way Sir William has, they say. He takes his time: leaves his prisoners for a day or two to think it over, and the clock strikes the night hours away, and in the darkness it's like being in a grave."

"By heaven!" ejaculated Mick. "I cannot bear the thought of anyone being treated so. There must be some way to get him out. If the Green Man can do it, why not us? Have you no notion at all as to how it might be done?"

"None," replied Cullen gloomily. "You could try to draw the guard off the door, perhaps, but ten to one you'd not succeed. It'll be the military who'll be guarding him, and they're well trained and mighty afraid of going against Sir William's orders. There's one lad, though," Cullen added, as though this thought had just dawned on him, "there's one of them whom I'm after knowing. He might let me have a word with Lenehan again if there was enough money in it to make the risk worth taking."

"I was afraid it would amount to money," said Mick in a disappointed voice. "I could try applying to my brother. If it was anyone else, it would be worth asking him to do something, for he's a deal of influence. But he wouldn't raise a finger for John Lenehan. I've heard him say that John's not much better than a murderer, for it was he who persuaded so many of our young men to take the United Oath, you know."

"Denny would say the same about yourself, Mister Mick.

No. You'd be best not to mention it to him." He sighed and turned away. "Oh, well! We'd best leave it, then.'

"No. Wait!" said Mick sharply. "I'll have to help John somehow. I've nothing to do this morning that will not wait. I'll ride down to the jail and try to see him."

"You might not be let in."

"I mean to try, at any rate."

"There's not much time, Mister Mick. If we're to get him clear away before Sir William's men use the torture on him, it'll have to be tomorrow night."

"Somehow," said Mick in an anguished tone, "somehow I've got to prevent that happening." He glanced at Cullen and said, "When can I see you again?"

Having made an appointment to meet Cullen later on that day, Mick set off at a brisk canter toward Clonmel.

KITTY HAD SPENT a happy morning walking with Mary and the dogs by the lakeside, watching Luke supervise the building of several ingenious hides from which the gentlemen were going to shoot the ducks on the following morning. Luke was seen to advantage among his own people, Kitty thought. Standing ankle-deep in boggy water, helping to devise a screen of lopped branches around a wooden platform, he looked younger and more carefree than she had ever seen him. From time to time he came over and spoke to Kitty and his small sister, explaining how the duck would fly in for the early-morning flight. "At least, that is what we hope," he added, smiling. "One can never be sure."

"I do not know how you can bear to shoot them," sighed Kitty, watching some other ducks skimming the water at the far end of the lake. "They are such lovely creatures that it seems a crime."

He laughed at her and went back to his work. It was only

later in the day, when the family sat down to a late luncheon, that the atmosphere became one of decided strain. The reason for this was that Mick, having ridden impetuously back from Clonmel, had rashly chosen to tell his brother about John Lenehan's troubles, and made a great scene about it when Luke flatly refused to help in any way. It would have been embarrassing enough for Kitty to be there, for to be an unwilling audience to a family argument is never a comfortable situation. But what made it worse was that Mick, failing to get any sympathy from Luke, turned to Kitty and appealed for her support. She would have been glad for any excuse to have left the room, but there was no escape.

"What would you do in my case, ma'am?" Mick reiterated. "John Lenehan is a friend of mine. Whatever Luke may choose to say about his politics (and it is monstrous unfair to blame him for what is past history), whatever Luke may say," he added, darting a dark glance at his brother, who was unconcernedly eating roast beef at the head of the table, "whatever he may say, there is surely nothing more despicable than someone who will not make a push to help an old friend?"

"John Lenehan is no friend of mine," said Luke without looking up. "Nor was he of yours, Mick. I do not call it friendship to make a rebel of you."

"John did not make me do anything. I was quite capable of thinking for myself."

"So I remember you to have said at the time," replied his brother dryly.

"At any rate," returned Mick, hastily abandoning this line of argument, "I was asking Lady Kitty for her opinion. I am already familiar with yours. Now, ma'am, give me an honest answer, if you please. If a friend of yours had been wrongfully imprisoned, and was about to be tortured, would you not be concerned?"

Kitty said slowly, "Of course I should. But how do you know he will be tortured? Can you not go and see him? You may well find that his plight is not as bad as you think."

Mr. Denny raised his dark head. And said quietly, "By the way, Mick, how do you know all this? Have you been seeing some other of your . . . er . . . friends?"

Mick looked uncomfortable. He said with an air of slightly labored nonchalance, "I have ways of learning things. And as for seeing John, I tried to do so this morning and they would not let me near him. The governor said that Fossick had given orders that no one was to see John . . ." He broke off, looked uncertainly at Kitty, and added, "If you do not believe me, ma'am, you should ask Sir William Fossick, for it is he who is at the bottom of the whole thing."

"I do not believe William would wrongfully imprison anyone," declared Kitty firmly. "Of course, if he were convinced that the man was a traitor, he would do his duty . . ." She reflected that William would undoubtedly be quite unswerving and determined to carry out his duties, but she did not believe that he would be vindictive. "I daresay," she added, "that he is quite as distressed as you are."

Mick forgot himself so far as to make a disbelieving noise that was halfway between a snort and a cough. "Aye, no doubt Fossick will be deeply grieved when he hears that his men have flogged John to death! Doubtless his heart will bleed . . ."

"You are talking a great deal of nonsense," retorted Kitty. "I do not think you can know William very well if you are willing to believe all these horrifying tales about him. Believe me, he is not at all an ogre. He is the most staid, painstaking, honest man—even," she added, smiling persuasively, her green eyes gleaming up at him through their fringed lashes, "even a little dull at times . . ."

Mick had perhaps already repented of his rudeness, for he

was looking down at his plate with something of the expression of a sullen schoolboy.

Glancing at Luke for support, Kitty found that he was regarding her rather piercingly, with an expression in his dark face which might almost have been sympathy. This was the first time she had sensed any softening in his casual, mocking attitude toward her, and she stretched out a slender hand to him in a supplicating gesture. "Anyone who is acquainted with William at all will know that he would certainly never do anything unlawful. Do you not agree with me, Mr. Denny?"

The warm look faded from his face before she had finished speaking. He said coolly, "I dare say your Ladyship is right. As deputy sheriff, Fossick would be bound to uphold the law, would he not? Now, ma'am, may I carve you another slice of beef?"

"No, thank you," replied Kitty, feeling as though she had been slapped. It had been plain from the first, of course, that her host regarded her without favor, but Kitty was not at all accustomed to being disliked or disapproved of (certainly not, at least, by the gentlemen of her acquaintance) and she had set herself to wooing him out of his initial attitude. She had worn her most modish gown for dinner on that first evening. She had drifted into the morning room, a breathtaking vision in a gown of the palest primrose muslin. With her hair gleaming in the candlelight, she flattered herself that she was looking well. The loquacious Lord Wandlebury had been rendered practically speechless for a few moments at the sight of her in that particular gown, and when he had been able to speak, he had called her his golden goddess and had begged her never to wear anything but that shade of pale yellow.

As Kitty came into the room, her eyes downcast and demure, Mick Denny had bowed over her hand and told her that she looked delightful. Luke, however, had merely bidden her good evening without much warmth and had straightway suggested that since she had obviously mistaken the season and was dressed for a heat wave, it might be as well to send upstairs for a shawl to put around her. He had no ambition, he announced odiously, to be saddled with a second invalid within forty-eight hours.

Kitty had been more amused than piqued at the time, but there was no doubt that it was becoming less and less gratifying to be treated like a tiresome foundling of whom he scarcely approved, and to have all her efforts to be friendly rebuffed.

"Then perhaps I may tempt your Ladyship to an apple," pursued Luke, breaking in upon her chagrined thoughts.

She thought, with a splutter of inward laughter, that he was plainly determined that she would not become ill through starvation either. "Thank you, sir," she replied in as indifferent and chilly a tone as his own, "but I do not wish for an apple."

"Luke!" insisted Mick in a voice of urgent supplication. "Only let me sell you my ring, the one that was Father's! If you were to give me even fifty guineas for it, I'll wager I could do a deal toward making John's situation less desperate . . ."

"I don't want your ring," replied Luke. "And I forbid you to sell it or pawn it elsewhere, if that is what you are considering." He eyed his younger brother very straightly for a moment. "Let us have an end to the subject."

"Now how would it be," said Kitty with a brightness that sounded spurious even to her own ears, "how would it be if I spoke to Sir William and asked him if you might visit your friend?"

There could be no doubt that Mick thought her suggestion to be a marvelous one. "Oh, Lady Kitty!" he breathed rapturously, "That would be above all things great. How can I ever thank you?"

"Easily," she returned, smiling. "When you find that Sir William is nothing like such an ogre as you suspect, you may beg my pardon."

Luke raised his eyeglass and surveyed Kitty through it. "You are very sure of yourself, and of your influence over our deputy sheriff," he remarked.

She smiled her slowest, most tantalizing smile. "Sir William has a kindness for me, I believe. Is that so extraordinary?"

Luke let his glass fall, so that it dangled from its narrow black ribbon. He said curtly, "I daresay there are a great many people who have a kindness for you, as you put it," and from his tone of voice it was plain that he did not think much of them, "but that does not mean to say that Fossick's kindness will extend itself to allowing Mick to see Lenehan in prison. He will allow nothing of the sort."

Kitty thought that Luke was coming it a bit strong. He might be at pains to show her that he was unimpressed by her charms and that he thought her a great nuisance, but he surely was not so arrogant as to suppose that his own taste was a measuring stick for everyone. It was time, she thought, that her host was taught a small lesson, and time for his family to learn that their highly respected head of the family was not entirely infallible.

She leaned forward and said in her sweetest voice, her drawl more marked than ever, "I will wager anything you like, Mr. Denny, that Sir William will allow Mick to visit his friend if I ask him to. But perhaps," she added dulcetly, "you are not a betting man?"

"A wager!" exclaimed Mick delightedly. "Famous! And if you are so certain that you are right, Luke, you must give her Ladyship good odds."

"I can hardly give her odds if I don't know what her Ladyship is prepared to hazard," retorted Luke, looking faintly amused and abominably sure of himself. "Come, ma'am, be a little more explicit. What do you mean by saying that you'll bet me anything I like? What do you suppose to be my heart's desire?"

It crossed Kitty's mind that if she had been rash enough to say anything of that sort to Wandlebury, he would have been quick enough to say what he wanted of her. She made a droll face at Mick and said, "Oh, how you love to put me in the wrong, Mr. Denny! Very well, I will freely confess that I have not the smallest notion of what you would like. So I will wager something that I like myself, instead. I have a diamond brooch upstairs of which I am particularly fond. Will that do?"

"And whatever shall I do with it when it is mine?" Luke demanded.

She could not resist saying sweetly, "Is there not one solitary female of your acquaintance who has a liking for jewelry, Mr. Denny? It is really very pretty, you know. It belonged to my grandmother, and the diamonds are good ones."

"Then it would be a pity to deprive you of it," said Luke smoothly.

"Oh, but if I really supposed that I would lose it," she retorted, shrugging her slim shoulders, "I should hazard something I cared for less. Let us hear what you are going to set against it, Mr. Denny. I am positively palpitating with interest. I do so dearly love winning something new and delightful in a wager."

"Yes? What will you put against Lady Kitty's brooch?" demanded Mick, his ill humor evaporated as though it had never been. "Have you laid eyes on anything here, Lady

(114)

Kitty, which you have taken a fancy to? Luke's gray horse, for instance?"

"Or one of the puppies?" put in Mary, who had been sitting round-eyed, drinking in all that was being said. "But if you were to win one of them, Lady Kitty, you might not be able to have it until it was weaned; and if you are travelling back to London before long, it will very likely be sick in the carriage. Puppies very often are, you know."

Kitty laughed. "That is a daunting thought, I admit. I think it had better be something a little more manageable." She turned to her host, who was leaning back in his chair, smiling faintly. "Is the choice really to be mine, Mr. Denny?"

The glitter in his dark eyes grew even more pronounced. "All Dennystown is at your mercy, ma'am," he assured her gravely.

"Heavens, Luke!" exclaimed Mick in mock alarm. "Have a care! If Fossick thought he could win Dennystown by letting me see John, he'd very likely jump at it. You know how he's always had an eye to our land by the river."

"How I would like to slap you when you speak so!" exclaimed Kitty, much incensed. "William would know nothing about it. This is my wager, and did you really think that I would be so dishonorable as to try to influence his decision . . ." She paused, overcome by a feeling of helplessness in face of their determined prejudice. "And anyway," she added indignantly, "if I were to win all Dennystown—and if you wonder what you would do with a brooch, Mr. Denny, I wish you will tell me what in the world I should do wih Dennystown—it would be myself who was winning it. What would William have to do with it?"

Mick had grown rather pink. "But I thought your Ladyship was going to marry him? Luke . . ." He turned toward his brother for support.

Luke frowned. The laughter had gone from his face. Instead, he was looking pensive and a trifle grim.

Kitty supposed that he was displeased with Mick for being tactless. Well, it served him right if he was embarrassed. If anyone had a right to be annoyed, it was surely herself. It was certainly quite possible that she might eventually agree to accept William's suit, but she did not at all wish to have all the world know about it before her mind was made up. She must somehow persuade the Dennys that she preferred not to have such things talked about.

Meanwhile, she said cheerfully, "Well, William did ask me to marry him, certainly. But that was fully five months ago, and he may be sadly disappointed when he sees me again."

"No fear of that," returned Mick, gazing at Kitty with open admiration.

"Well, I do hope not," she returned, laughing. "It has always seemed to me to be a sad fate to be jilted."

"What's jilted?" inquired Mary.

"If you ask so many pert questions," said Luke, not unkindly, "you may very well find out, my child." Then, turning to Kitty, he said briskly, "I think we should agree to forget about this wager, ma'am. It will be better so."

She laughed at him. "Oh? So you are beginning to cry off, are you sir? Well, I do not blame you. You are so certain to lose."

He stood up, looking gravely down at her from his great height. Once again she felt that he was regarding her with a kind of sympathy, almost as though he were sorry for her. He said quietly, "I suggested to Fossick that he should come here rather earlier than our other guests. We may expect to see him in an hour or so, I believe, so if you will excuse me now, ma'am, I've some farm matters to see to." And without waiting to hear whether he had gained her permission or not, he left the room.

(116)

CHAPTER TEN

LUKE CAME IN from the upper meadows to be told that the deputy sheriff was on the point of arriving. He strode into the hall, was greeted by the sound of men marching, of horses' hooves, and of wheels scrunching on the gravel. He went quickly through the front door. Mick was already there, standing on the upper step, and the two brothers waited while Sir William Fossick rode up at the head of no less than twenty red-coated men. At the rear of the party came Sir William's traveling chaise, drawn by four glossy chestnuts.

"Luke," muttered Mick in a furious undertone, "what in the world does the fellow mean by bringing this rabble here? Does he mean to quarter them here while he waits for Lady

Kitty to go with him? You do not, surely, mean to stand for it?"

Luke gave no sign of having heard his brother's remarks. Sir William had ridden alongside them. The sergeant at the head of the double file of men roared out an order to halt, and the whole party stamped to a standstill. A groom ran forward to take Sir William's bridle, and he dismounted with an agility which was really remarkable in so large a man.

Luke said gravely, "You are welcome to Dennystown, Fossick." He nodded slightly but did not hold out his hand.

Sir William made a rather sweeping bow and said, "Your servant, Denny." His blue eyes sought out Mick, who was hanging back with his arms folded and his lips tightly set, and added, "So this is young Mick! You'll be pleased to be back in Ireland after so long a spell abroad, eh?" He laughed his loud, hearty laugh. "And mighty fashionable you've become, too! Did Weston make that coat?"

"Mick!" said Luke. There was something of a rasp in his voice. His brother made a stiff bow. "You must forgive my brother, Fossick," said Luke, raising his brows, "Truth to tell, we are all dazzled by the magnificence of your . . . er . . . escort." His dark eyes swept coolly from one to another of the smartly uniformed but distinctly villainous-looking crew who were standing rigidly to attention on the gravel sweep below him. "We were not aware that you always traveled in such state."

Sir William shrugged his shoulders. "You would not, surely, wish me to put Lady Kitty and her party at risk by neglecting to give her a proper escort?"

"All these men just to take Lady Kitty to Mount Come-ragh Lodge, Fossick?" exclaimed Mick incredulously. "Your experiences in the late rebellion must have made you over-nervous."

Sir William surveyed the young man for a second time.

There was a smile upon his fair face, a smile which did not reach his blue eyes. "I like to be prepared for anything. You must learn to tell the difference between prudence and nervousness."

"You have nothing to be nervous about at Dennystown while you are here as my guest," said Luke, directing a quelling look at Mick. "And Mick is perfectly right, you had no need to bring an army with you. However . . ."

"Are you trying to tell me, Denny, that my men are not welcome here?"

"They are welcome so long as they conduct themselves properly," returned Luke. "No doubt you will be able to guarantee that?"

"Certainly," replied Sir William stiffly. "My men are well trained, and will do as I say. But they will need food and accommodation."

"It shall be given them." Luke turned to the groom, who had been staring in evident bewilderment at the deputy sheriff's men. He gave orders that the soldiers were to be bestowed in the barrack room beyond the stables and were to be given everything they needed. "And send Paddy Joe to me as soon as they are settled."

The sergeant looked toward Sir William, who nodded none too graciously; and as the group moved off to the stables, followed by the chaise, Luke invited the deputy sheriff to step inside the house.

Inside, Sir William looked about him with some curiosity, noting with satisfaction the modest, old-fashioned furnishings of the hall and comparing the place with the lofty paneled apartment which formed the entrance to his own house. Presently he was ushered into a long, sunlit room where a turf fire glowed at the far end. The fireplace was wide and made of stone, and the rugs which lay at intervals upon the polished wood floor were faded and worn.

There was little to admire here, he reflected as he received a glass of Madeira from Luke's hand, and still less to covet. The room was furnished more for use than for elegance, with scarcely any ornaments or knickknacks. A riding crop had been flung down upon a table top, and a spaniel snored drunkenly on a cushioned chair by the fire. Luke nudged the dog off and offered his guest a seat.

Sir William declined the offer. He stood by the fire, sipping his wine. Presently, since neither Luke nor his brother showed any disposition to break the silence, he said, smiling, "Now, tell me the truth, Denny. Here I am, come to Dennystown at your most kind and pressing invitation"—the irony in his voice was marked—"so now you can afford to be frank with me. Is Lady Kitty really here?"

"Well, of course she is!" replied Mick, opening his eyes. "Why . . ." Then he gave a startled laugh. "Did you think we were trying to roast you? Or did you fear that we'd hold you to ransom here, and so that's why you brought an army with you? Oh, famous!"

"Let us say that I was keeping an open mind," returned Sir William suavely.

"What if it should be a jest?" demanded Mick. "Is that a crime?"

"You forget, Mick," put in Luke solemnly. "Fossick represents the law in these parts. He is not to be trifled with. Is that not so, Fossick?"

Sir William looked from Luke to his younger brother, and back again. "You are perfectly right, Denny," he said at last. "Young Mick would do well to remember that the law is neither to be mocked nor to be flouted. I mean precisely what I say."

Luke raised his brows. "Do I detect a threatening note in your voice, Fossick? Do, I beg of you, be a little plainer. Are you suggesting that any of us here have been . . . er . . . trifling with the law."

Mick chuckled. "No. You are quite mistaken, Luke. Fossick merely thinks that Lady Kitty is a figment of our imaginations!"

"Then you must have a high opinion of our inventive powers," said Luke. He raised his head, listening intently for a moment, and then added, "I think you are shortly going to be put out of your suspense, Fossick. Though I must break it to you that Lady Kitty's little boy is not yet well enough to travel."

"Not well enough . . ." repeated Sir William, frowning. "You did not tell me that!"

"Oh, I daresay he'll be all right," said Mick easily, "if he's wrapped up warmly. Aunt Biddy thought that another day or two is all he'll need; and after all it's not more than twenty miles to Fossick's place."

"Unfortunately," retorted Sir William, the color of his ruddy complexion deepening noticeably, "unfortunately, circumstances do not permit that I entertain Lady Kitty at Mount Comeragh Lodge. I intend to send her to Dublin in my chaise; but of course, if the boy is ill . . ."

"Good God!" exclaimed Mick. "You don't mean to say . . ."

"Mick!" Luke's voice held a warning. "Go and inform her Ladyship that Fossick is in here. She may not have been told."

"But . . ."

"At once!"

"Oh, all right," the young man said, turning to go. "But don't blame me, Fossick, if I also warn her that she's to be shipped back to Dublin like an unwanted piece of baggage."

(121)

"Do as you please," replied Sir William coldly. "She will have to be told by someone."

"Masterly," said Luke. "It is so much easier to leave the telling of disagreeable news to others."

Sir William swung round, glaring. "Do you really think I dare not tell her myself, Denny?"

Luke smiled lazily into the deputy sheriff's angry face. "How you jump to conclusions, Fossick. I never doubted your valor for a moment."

"Well, I'm not going to say a word," said Mick fiercely, from the doorway. "I think it's disgusting. And I very much hope that Lady Kitty gives you the trimming you deserve."

"Mick!" Kitty's sweetly drawling voice broke in upon his angry tirade. "Mick! Do not say that you have fallen out with poor William already?" She came lightly and swiftly into the room, dressed in a high-waisted dark green riding habit, her gloves, whip, and a plumed hat held in one hand, her gleaming gold hair only a little disheveled. She held out her free hand to Sir William. "Dearest William!" she said warmly. "How delightful to see you again. But you need not have brought half His Majesty's army to fetch me to Mount Comeragh Lodge, you know! I could scarcely ride into the yard just now, there were soldiers stamping all over it. Mary and I were all in a quake that your men would arrest us."

Sir William took her hand and bowed over it slowly. It almost seemed to him, at that moment, that he must be dreaming. He said mechanically, "Only traitors need fear my men, ma'am. I trust there are none at Dennystown."

She smiled up at him teasingly. "Well, I am no traitor, William. Yet I confess that one of your men looked so ferociously at me that I quailed. You plainly did not choose any of them for their beauty."

He gave a loud laugh. He was trying to shake off the feeling that none of this was real. "You are perfectly right, ma'am. I choose my men for very different qualities than their looks, I can tell you that."

"Well, I do not doubt that you could tell me," said Kitty lightly. "But pray do not, for you know that I detest military talk. Tell me instead how you are, William. It is an age since I saw you. How do you go on?"

If the deputy sheriff had been in the habit of giving rein to his emotions, he might well have groaned aloud at that moment. Never had Kitty looked more desirable. Never had she smiled more warmly at him, and looked at him with just that look of tenderness in her green eyes. And never before had she been so utterly forbidden. He answered her questions very much at random, scarcely knowing what he said, and all the while wrestling with a fierce desire to throw Lord Comeragh's offer away and to take Kitty back to Mount Comeragh Lodge.

"But you have not asked me how I came to be here?" she chided him, accepting a glass of wine from Luke and sitting down on a small sofa at a little distance from the fire. She patted the cushioned seat at her side, inviting Sir William to sit there. "I have had the most horrid adventures, William."

"Yes. Tell us about them, Lady Kitty," begged Mick. "We have so far only had Luke's account of your meeting at the Castle, and one may never place much reliance on Luke's stories."

Luke, sitting in a winged chair on the other side of the fireplace, merely eyed his brother quizzically. He said nothing.

"You went to the Castle?" repeated Sir William, blinking. "You met at the Castle?"

"Why yes, William," said Kitty, turning toward the deputy sheriff and taking care not to glance in the direction of her host. She met a glance of such warmth and desire in Sir William's blue eyes that she was almost dismayed. It was one thing to be gay and welcoming to William, and to show that odious Mr. Denny that she was appreciated by some people, even if he did not find her tolerable himself, but it would never do to give William too much encouragement. She did not wish to be committed to anything yet. She said reproachfully, "How was I to know that your house and the Castle had the same names? You never warned me. Besides, I had rather hoped you would send a carriage to meet me at Waterford."

"I could not do that, ma'am,' said Sir William defensively and almost accusingly, "for I had no notion you were coming." But his mind was already groping with the extraordinary circumstance that Kitty and Denny had met, of all places, in Mount Comeragh Castle. What was the meaning of it? He felt quite bewildered, though he did not show it. "You say that you met Denny in Mount Comeragh Castle? I can scarcely credit it."

She shuddered dramatically. "Oh, it was a veritable nightmare! I have never been so terrified in my life."

"Nonsense!" put in Luke calmly. He glanced at Sir William's astonished face, apparently unaware of the fierce suspicion which seethed under his look of astonishment, and added, "Her Ladyship reveled in the Castle, Fossick. There was everything there that she could wish for—a ruined mansion, cobwebs, bats flitting here and there; and if anything was missing in the way of headless specters, no doubt Lady Kitty's fertile imagination was easily able to supply it."

"There was no need for me to imagine anything, Mr. Denny," retorted Kitty, raising her chin. "You looked so villainous and threatening, I thought you were a dangerous lunatic, at least." She turned to Sir William and assured him earnestly, "Really, William! Mr. Denny looked quite wild-eyed."

"No doubt I was startled," retorted Luke, still eying the

deputy sheriff. "You see, Fossick," he explained, "her Lady-ship took me for one of your mad relations. I was so . . . overcome by the honor, you know, that perhaps I may be forgiven for looking a trifle frenzied?"

Sir William said sourly, "I really have not the slightest notion what this all means. May I hope that sooner or later someone will make it clear to me?"

"But, William, I am just telling you," protested Kitty, laughing up at him. "My coachman mistook the address, you see, and there I was in the middle of the night, confronted by Mr. Denny. He spoke to me in such a threatening way that I swooned . . ."

"In the middle of the night?" repeated Sir William sharply. "I see why Lady Kitty came to be there, perhaps, but why were you there also, Denny? I had heard the place was generally believed to be haunted, and that no one will go there except in daylight."

"Oh, as to that," supplied Mick, chuckling, "Luke assured us that he was looking for ghosts. So that's your explanation, Fossick."

The deputy sheriff had not taken his eyes from Luke's face. "It's not an explanation which I find in the least accepta-ble, however," he murmured. "What is your own explana-tion, Denny? Or do you not have one ready for me?"

"Since when, Fossick, must I explain my movements to you?" inquired Luke mildly, helping himself to snuff in a casual way. "I was in my own house, on my own land. There is nothing to explain, so far as I can see."

There was a pause. Then, suddenly, Sir William laughed. "You are very sure of yourself, aren't you, Denny? Well, I shall not press you; I am in no hurry. And as you say, you were in your own house . . ." He leaned back and smiled broadly. "I am quite happy to bide my time."

"Your conversation is sometimes quite bewildering, Fossick," said Luke, raising his eyeglass and surveying the deputy sheriff's flushed but complacent face for a few moments. "But I wish you would enlighten me. What sinister plots do you hope to uncover?"

Sir William said slowly, "It has merely occurred to me, Denny, that the Castle might be a convenient place for anyone to hide if they were anxious to escape the eye of the law. That is all."

Luke shrugged his shoulders. "Well, as a matter of fact, Fossick, you are nearer the truth than you know. The task I had set myself that night was rather more in your line than in mine, for I had discovered that a certain undesirable person had been using the Castle for a lodging place. I had gone to remove him, but, instead, I found Lady Kitty."

"Another undesirable person?" she supplied swiftly. "Mr. Denny, your company is indeed horridly salutary."

But neither Luke nor Mick nor the deputy sheriff gave any sign of having heard this quip, for Luke was once again wholly occupied with taking another of his extravagant and messy pinches of snuff, and the other two men were eying him with considerable interest.

Mick said quickly, "Oh, so that was who . . ." He stopped short and swallowed nervously. "Luke, you might have told me."

"Told you what?" demanded Sir William in a voice as sharp as a knife.

Mick stammered a little as he said, "Why, nothing important, really. I just had not known till this moment who it was that Luke had gone to meet."

"And who was it?"

Mick hesitated, glanced at his brother, and said, shrugging, "It was a man called Cullen, I've reason to think."

"Cullen?" echoed Sir William sharply, looking taken

aback. "Cullen? If Cullen is a friend of yours, young man, I begin to have my doubts as to your loyalty."

Luke said flatly and dismissively, "Mick is occasionally a fool, Fossick, but no villain. You may be sure of that."

"Ah! But how well do you know your brother, Denny?" demanded Sir William. "Can you be sure that you are as much in his confidence as you think you are?"

"I never supposed myself to be in his confidence," replied Luke. "Why should I be indeed?"

Sir William gave vent to an angry sound, and Kitty, sensing that some sort of duel was being fought yet hardly comprehending what it was about, said sweetly, "William, you must not allow yourself to be tormented by Mr. Denny. To be angry with him is, I assure you, only to oblige him."

"I am not in the least angry, ma'am," he retorted. "I am merely curious to know how it is that young Mick should be consorting with an acknowledged traitor and spy like Cullen!"

"William," she chided him, laying a slim hand upon his arm, "Mr. Denny is roasting you. It is a tradition here at Dennystown that all visitors must be teased and tantalized until they do not know what they are about. It gives the Denny family such delightful entertainment, you know, that one really must not grudge it them." She turned her head and smiled at Luke. "You see, they live so very quietly here, so far from all the dissipations of the town, that they are forced to make their own diversions. Is that not so, Mr. Denny?"

"Very astute of you, ma'am," he conceded, smiling his tight-lipped smile. "As you say, even rustics deserve some joy in their lives."

"Deserve?" she queried with an air of mystification. "Did I say that?"

"Now, look here . . ." began Sir William, clearing his throat.

"No, William." Once more Kitty laid a restraining hand on his arm. "Please do not pursue such a tedious subject any more. And you, Mick," she added, "be so good as to leave us now, for I wish to discuss my own affairs with Sir William, and while you are here to divert his attention I shall never learn how or when he means to convey me to Mount Comeragh Lodge."

CHAPTER ELEVEN

"YES," SAID LUKE as Mick made a quick, rather offended bow to Kitty and strode hastily out of the room. "Enlighten us, Fossick. What are your plans for her Ladyship?"

"I understood you to say, Denny, that Lady Kitty's child is ill and may not travel for a few days," said Sir William, trying to win himself time in which to arrange his thoughts. He turned to Kitty. "I am sorry to hear it, ma'am. Is he so very bad?"

She shrugged her shoulders. "Oh, Robert will be quite able to travel in two days' time. Mr. Denny is merely looking grave because he is afraid of having to keep us even as long as that. If you can stay here these next two nights, William, you may take us all home with you. So long as Robert is kept warm, I do not think he will take harm from that short journey."

Sir William's high white neckcloth appeared, in that moment, to have been tied too tightly for his comfort. He fingered the folds nervously, swallowed, and murmured that he would have liked it better if her Ladyship had given him more warning of her approach.

"Oh, dear," said Kitty, looking taken aback. "I wrote to you, William . . ." She paused, looked at him in a considering way, and said quietly, "What is the matter? Are you not pleased to see me here, after all?"

This was going too fast for him. "Pray do not think for a moment, ma'am, that I am not entranced to see you . . ."

"You certainly do not seem to be entranced. If it is not convenient for us to visit you, we may as easily put up at your nearest inn, you know."

"What a circuitous fellow you are, Fossick," remarked Luke in his driest voice. "Why not give her Ladyship the truth, and put us all out of our suspense?"

"I do not see," said the deputy sheriff, furiously turning on his host, "that this has anything whatsoever to do with you, Denny. If you had any conduct at all, you would leave us alone!"

"I daresay I would, if I had any," Luke agreed cordially.

Kitty drew an unsteady breath. There was a hollow feeling in the pit of her stomach. She had been so counting on William as a source of support, looking forward to laying down the tiresome ordering of her own affairs, if only for a season. She said in a low voice, "Yes. Do be plain with me, William."

Sir William felt himself maneuvered into a false position. Of course it was necessary to tell Kitty that she must not stay in the county, but to have to do so with Denny lounging there, sneering at his dicomfiture, was less than tolerable. He glared at Luke again and said, "Once again, Denny, will you be good enough to leave us?"

Kitty opened her green eyes very wide. She had herself in hand again, and was in no mind to show her sense of desolation to either of them. "Oh, no!" she protested. "Do not go away, Mr. Denny. I have really no wish to be private with William."

"Now, ma'am," Sir William objected, "do you mean to say that you are willing to discuss our intimate affairs in front of Denny? I thought you had more sensibility."

"Intimate?" she murmured mischievously. "Oh, I never have intimate affairs, William dearest. My on-goings are always known to all the world, as you are very well aware. Come. You evidently are about to tell me some bad tidings, so please get it over quickly. You need not try to spare my feelings, truly you need not."

"Your feelings, ma'am?" he echoed savagely, forgetting his careful self-control. She was actually daring to laugh at him, this devilish female who had haunted his dreams for months. She had always treated him abominably, eluding him when he most wanted her, laughing her silver laughter until he had almost run mad. And now, when she ought by rights to be mortified by the consequences of her precipitate behavior, she did nothing but laugh and mock at him. "Your feelings, ma'am," he said again, lashing out at her in his rage and frustration. "I do not believe you ever had any! How was it, may I ask, that you tore yourself away from Wandlebury? Did you go too far, even for his careless sense of propriety? Or did he tire of your faithless flirting with all and sundry?"

Her pointed face, so pale a moment before, was suddenly aflame. She put a hand to her cheek as though to ward off a blow.

"Say what you have to say, Fossick," said Luke curtly. "And then, if her Ladyship will excuse us, I will have you shown to your room." He got up and pulled on the bell rope which hung beside the chimney piece.

Kitty looked at Sir William very straightly. She said gravely, "Yes, William, if you please, do not prevaricate any more."

It was almost a relief to tell her. "You cannot come to Mount Comeragh Lodge, ma'am. It will not do."

"Why may I not?"

"Because," he replied evenly, looking at the floor, "I am about to enter into an engagement of marriage with Lord Comeragh's niece. Our betrothal will be announced within the week, so, under the circumstances, it would hardly be suitable for me to entertain your Ladyship . . ." There was a pause, and when she said nothing, he added defensively, "It is too bad that you did not give me more warning, ma'am, for I would not for the world have had you journey all this way . . ."

"No. It must be shockingly awkward for you," she said, gazing down at her clasped hands, her face hidden. "How fortunate, indeed, that my coachman mistook the address of your house . . ."

"I did not mean that it was awkward for me . . ." he began: and when she glanced up at him, with unbelief in her green eyes, he began a labored explanation as to how he would not for the world have wished to do such an ungentlemanly thing as to send her Ladyship back to Dublin, but that there was really no help for it, under the circumstances. No one regretted it more than he, he assured her earnestly.

His peroration was becoming more and more tangled, so it was a relief to him when a manservant appeared at the door of the morning room and he was obliged to break it off. Luke suggested that the deputy sheriff might like to see his room so that he could change out of his riding clothes. Sir William bowed to Kitty, and with considerable feelings of relief, prepared to leave the room. He had reached the door when she spoke.

"William."

He stopped and turned. She was smiling at him and holding out her hand. "I wish you very happy," she said in her lilting, gentlest voice. "Indeed I do."

Luke went with his guest into the hall. When he had seen the deputy sheriff on his way up the stairs, he came back into the morning room to find Kitty standing with her back to him. Her head was bent and she seemed to be studying the glowing turf on the hearth. When he had all but reached her, she turned. Her lips were smiling, but he saw that her green eyes were brilliant with unshed tears. She dashed a hand across her eyes and said huskily, "Well, Mr. Denny? I hope you are pleased. What a delightful satisfaction it must be for you to have seen a famous jilt being paid back in her own coin!" She held out her hand to him and said, "You may now feel revenged for all the trouble I have been!"

He took her slender, ringed hand in his large brown one. There was, she found, something immeasurably comfortable and safe about the way he held it; and since she was always suspicious of the true nature of comfort, she said with an attempt at lightness, "We have been nothing but a tiresome nuisance, you must admit."

"Very tiresome," he agreed. There was an almost caressing note in his deep voice. "You have turned us all upside down. I have been wishing these two days or more that I'd never set eyes on you."

"I knew that I could count on you to say something salutary, Mr. Denny. Please release my hand."

"In a moment."

"Now!" she protested, trying to pull away from him. She said with a sob in her voice, "It is . . . ungentlemanly of you

(133)

to force yourself upon me, just when I am feeling dashed to the ground . . ."

He released her hand. "I had some notion of holding your hand to comfort you," he said. "But come to think of it, I'd be better to congratulate you and Fossick on a lucky escape. I can think of no more ill-matched couple."

"Oh!" she exclaimed, reanimated by indignation at this monstrously unfeeling speech. "So now you are presuming to give me advice on whom to marry?"

"I'd certainly advise you not to marry Fossick," he told her, looking down at her furious face and smiling thinly. "I'd have thought your own common sense would tell you that it would never do."

"I must be deficient in common sense, then."

"I daresay that must be the case," he agreed with infuriating cordiality. "But never mind. You have been preserved from your folly this time, and by the time some other man loses his head over you, you may have learned a little more sense. Next time you decide to marry, you should endeavor to look a little farther than the cut of his coat and the way he arranges his neckcloth."

She said swiftly, "At least I shall not choose to marry a man who spills snuff all down himself and smells of the stables!"

"No? But I thought you liked horses."

She had to quell a sudden, irrational urge to laugh. He was quite outrageous. "Certainly I like horses, but I cannot bring myself to admire a man who comes into the house in all his dirt as you do, sir."

He said curiously, "And are you so anxious to bring yourself to admire me, ma'am?"

She giggled. She had not meant to do so, but the laughter bubbled up in her despite her sense of outrage. "Oh, you are impossible," she said crossly. "Of course you may be as slovenly as you like, for all I care. I was merely saying, only you chose to mistake my meaning, that I like a man to be fastidious in his dress and polished in his manners . . ." She broke off, seeing the unholy gleam of laughter which lit his dark eyes. She felt herself blushing, a thing she had not done for ages, and turned away to hide her confusion. "At any rate," she added petulantly, "this is a foolish conversation, and I am not amused."

"No? Then why did you laugh?"

"I was not laughing, or rather . . ." She turned back to him, abandoning the struggle to suppress another traitorous bubble of hilarity, and said weakly, "Oh, do not tease me any more, sir. You were quite right when you said I wanted comfort, indeed you were! I hardly know whether I want to laugh or cry."

He took her hand again, turning it palm upward in his hard fingers. "No. You haven't the least idea what you want, have you? You are lost and flighty, and altogether too damned attractive for your own good. What you need is a man to keep you in control, but what you will choose for yourself is some meek satellite who'll never so much as rumple your hair or cause you a moment's anxiety. And shall I tell you how it will be? No. Keep still!" as she struggled to free her hand for a second time. "You know how it will be yourself, don't you? You will hunt down your tame husband, polish him to a fine sheen, and you'll be bored to madness within a year."

"If you mean that I tried to hunt William Fossick, it was no such thing," she retorted. She was trembling in his hold, and was oddly reluctant to look up at him. "It was no such thing, I assure you."

"You traveled all the way from London in pursuit of him, did you not?"

"Yes. But . . ."

(135)

"You should be thanking heaven on your knees that your quarry has escaped, you know. Believe me, Fossick will be happier with his little heiress. He will bully her, I daresay, and greatly enjoy the prosperity and consequence of being heir to all the Comeragh wealth; and she, for her part, will be content to live in the wilds of Ireland and people the county with little Fossicks. Do not try to tell me that you would ever live that kind of life!"

"William assured me that we would stay only part of the year . . ." she began, and then said haughtily, "But that is none of your concern, Mr. Denny. And I am able to arrange my own affairs without any more impertinent advice from you, let me tell you!"

"You do not like advice, do you, ma'am? All you want is acquiescence; and for a while I daresay that Fossick might have been besotted enough to oblige you. But not for long, I think. Very well," he added nonchalantly, "arrange your affairs in any way you like—that's a novel euphemism for catching a husband, I must say!—but when you find yourself married a month or two and are already seeking for means of relieving the tedium, you may remember what I say. Johnny Harcombe may have had singular tastes in some ways, and probably he led you a dance, but even he must have been a more stimulating mate for you than the safe, brow-beaten sheep you are looking for."

Great as was her chagrin and mortification at being spoken to in such a way, she could not resist saying, "Oh? Did you know Johnny?"

He looked down at her, again with that odd comprehending look. "Yes, I knew him. A pretty fellow, was he not?"

She said defiantly, "I loved him, you know. Really, I think he was the only man I have ever truly loved."

He said gravely, "Then you must have been very un-

(136)

happy. So you mean never to be caught like that again? Is that it?"

That was so painfully near to the truth, that Kitty was forced to deny it. "I do not know what you mean."

"No?"

"No!" She almost spat the denial at him. "And I'll tell you this, Mr. Denny! If you were the last man on earth, I would certainly never be tempted to marry you! You are rude, uncivilized, odious, and altogether . . . unspeakable!"

He looked down into her flushed face, smiling wickedly, at the same time taking possession of both her hands in a firm grasp. "But I have not asked you to marry me."

"Let me go at once, sir!" Her voice was no more than a breathless, outraged whisper. "You are abominable!"

"And rude, and odious," he supplied heartlessly. "You have given me a fine dressing, haven't you? My character is in shreds. Well, I will return the compliment and tell you what I think of you. You are spoiled and hot-tempered and masterful, ma'am, and it's high time someone took you in hand. In fact, it's as well that you are leaving us soon, else I should be tempted to do so myself. You are outrageously beautiful, and I'd like to beat you."

Kitty found herself both weak and breathless, and quite unable to command words which would be sufficiently pungent to express her feelings. He smiled his thin, mocking smile and let go of her hands so abruptly that she almost lost her balance. A moment later she found herself clasped in his arms.

"I have been wanting to do this since the moment I first saw you," he said. And bending his head he kissed her full and lingeringly on her lips.

CHAPTER TWELVE

SIR WILLIAM FOSSICK'S private army, as Captain George Dillon called it, was housed in the barrack room. This barnlike building was situated behind the stables, next door to the forge and the various outbuildings where sheepskins were cured and stored and where the carpenter and the other skilled persons worked by day. The barrack room boasted an open fire, and was otherwise furnished only with some rough benches and a heap of straw mattresses, and it was here that anyone who came to Dennystown in need of shelter and a place to sleep would come.

It had been occupied already by a ragged family from the western hills, and these poor people watched fearfully as twenty red-coated men trooped in upon them. They removed themselves from before the fire so that the privileged military might warm themselves. Paddy Joe, a bow-legged elderly man whose word was law in the stables, and who was generally thought to wield more power at Dennystown than anyone except the family, beckoned to the father of this brood and told him that they had better bed down in a loose box for the night. With alacrity they gathered their few belongings and followed Paddy Joe to their new refuge.

The soldiers were given food and ale, and were then left severely alone. Their occasional bursts of rough laughter and rumbling talk were heard until late into the night, but they made no attempt to leave their lodging or to make themselves obnoxious. Nevertheless, no one could forget that they were there. The reputation of Sir William Fossick's men was too well known in the countryside for anyone to be easy in their minds while they were so near. Paddy Joe gave orders for all the stores to be locked up and all doors to be barred; and he took three of his most reliable men to sleep at various points around the stables.

The gentlemen from the house set out on horseback well before dawn, and it was midday before they came back again, muddy and soaked to the skin but in high spirits. After consuming a hearty meal they all straggled into the morning room, some with tankards still in hand, and Kitty was regaled with tales of how many duck had been shot and how Sir William had particularly distinguished himself that morning.

"Aye, Fossick put us all to shame this morning," said Judge Moore. "He's one of those men who seems to succeed at everything he turns his hand to. How do you do it, Fossick? What's the secret?"

Sir William laughed, disclaiming and saying that his skill that morning had been nothing out of the common way. He was nonetheless in excellent spirits and was feeling very well pleased with himself. He had received word from Matt Cullen that Mick had as good as swallowed the bait which had been offered him, and he had spoken with Kitty on his return from the shoot and been assured by her that she was leaving Dennystown the following morning. All in all, it really did seem things were going his way.

Mick was in considerably lower spirits than usual. He had passed a miserable morning, half submerged among some reeds, with nothing to shoot at. Even the sight and sound of the wild birds streaming in and the flashes and bangs of the guns in the semi-darkness, which normally would have thrilled and excited him, had done nothing to remove his depression; and with the cold rain stinging his face and his tormented thoughts for company, he had been only too glad when the shoot had been declared at an end.

He walked back to the house with Father James, who was a fanatical wild-fowler, and listened to him expounding a theory that Luke should have built three more hides on the south shore of the lake. Mick answered the priest rather at random, caring very little about such things in his present preoccupied state.

Presently he managed to have a word with Kitty. "I don't know whether it would be any good now, ma'am," he said tentatively, "but if you remember, you did suggest that you would speak to Fossick about John Lenehan—just to ask if I might see him, you know?"

"Oh!" said Kitty, looking doubtfully across the room at the deputy sheriff. "Well, at the risk of yet another setdown, I will try my luck. I am becoming quite inured to such things."

She moved away from Mick, and presently engaged Sir William in conversation, asking him to explain to her the meaning of all the political talk that was going on around them. Judge Moore and Mr. Pennefather were trying to convince Luke that he would be doing the very best thing for himself and his people by supporting Mr. Pitt's proposed

Union with England. It would be the best way, they said, for furthering the cause of the Roman Catholics in Ireland; indeed, Mr. Pitt had as good as promised that Catholic emancipation would come as part of the Union negotiations. Luke was plainly not entirely of the same mind as the other two gentlemen, though he listened civilly enough to all they had to say. Only when Mr. Pennefather said jovially that they'd see Luke sitting as Member for the County yet, did Luke shake his head and declare that he had more to do with his time than to traipse backward and forward to Westminster.

Kitty, who had heard these conversations going on from time to time since the gentlemen had first arrived, begged Sir William to make matters plain to her. Why was Mr. Pitt so bent on contriving the Union? Had not Ireland already a parliament of its own? Please would he tell her what it was about?

Sir William was nothing loath. As Lord Comeragh's man, he was as keen on the Union as anyone (indeed, he had secret hopes that his own part in bringing it about might win him a peerage). He held forth for some time on the subject without greatly enlightening Kitty's ignorance, but giving her a chance to listen with rapt interest. He was no more immune to this flattering attention than he had ever been, and he was moreover both relieved and grateful that Kitty should apparently bear him no grudge for treating her in a manner which even he could not call anything but churlish. He smiled down at her and squeezed her hand briefly, saying, "You know, ma'am, I have always said that you were an exceptional woman, and now I'm doubly sure of it."

"Good gracious, William! I assure you that I am nothing of the kind. To tell you the truth, I was turning you up sweet because there is something I want you to do for me."

"I assure you, ma'am, that if there is anything in my power . . ." he began.

She looked around the room. "It seems to me," she murmured, "that most things lie in your power in this county, William. I had no idea until I arrived at Dennystown that you were such a man of . . . consequence. And do you know," she added, as if it were a matter for wonderment, "I believe they are all a little afraid of you here."

He laughed his short barking laugh. "I shouldn't wonder. I shouldn't wonder at all."

"Well, I have been doing my best to tell everyone that you are not at all the ogre you are made out to be," she assured him, smiling at him as though they shared a secret. "If I could persuade Mick, for instance, that you are really not at all a monster, but are on the other hand most generous and human, I should feel my journey into Ireland had not been wholly wasted."

"Now, how am I to take that, ma'am?" he asked levelly.

She said gaily, "Why, William, it is only a little thing I am going to ask of you, so do not look so severely at me. You will be giving credence to all the tales I have been hearing of you."

"What tales, ma'am?"

She said reproachfully, "You do not think I have been foolish enough to believe any of them, do you? If you will oblige me by allowing Mick to visit some friend of his in jail, I believe that even he will be able to see how he has misjudged you."

She saw a gleam of comprehension in Sir William's blue eyes—it might almost have been a look of triumph. "Ah," he said. "He wishes to see a man by the name of Lenehan, is that the case?" She nodded. "Then why," he demanded quite loudly, "why does young Mick not ask me himself, eh? Does he lack the courage?"

The deputy sheriff's ringing tones brought every head round to look at him. Mick came forward with a nervous, jerking stride, almost like a puppet pulled by strings. "Indeed, it was not that, sir!" he said eagerly. "It was just that I did not think you would listen to me."

"I never refuse to listen to reasonable requests, young man. Have you ever had any reason to doubt that?"

Mick swallowed and said, "N . . . no, sir. But you see . . ."

"But you preferred to leave the asking to Lady Kitty, eh?"

Mick had grown rather red in the face. He glanced at Kitty, who made a droll face at him and said nothing at all. There did not seem to be anything for Mick to say either; so he waited.

"What is this favor you are asking of me?" rapped out Sir William suddenly. "Come now! Surely you can speak for yourself?"

Meeting the deputy sheriff's eye with a look which was fiery enough, Mick said, "I should be grateful indeed, sir, if you would allow me to see John Lenehan. I tried to see him yesterday, but they told me he was allowed no visitors." Mick drew a breath and said in a low, imploring tone, "There is a rumor in the town, sir, that you mean to have John flogged tomorrow, that you believe him to be in possession of information about the . . . the . . ."

"About the Green Man, as he is called," supplied the deputy sheriff suavely. "Well?"

Mick said desperately, "It is not possible for John to know anything about the Green Man. He was out of Ireland before the fellow saved . . . I mean, before any of the abductions . . ." He broke off and said earnestly and with some dignity, "In any case, sir, John Lenehan is old and not in good health. It would kill him to be flogged. I did not ask you myself, and I know it must have an odd appearance, but if Lady Kitty is right, and if you are indeed a just and kindly man, you must see that John is in no state to be maltreated."

Sir William said slowly, "I am almost persuaded by your fervor." He paused, and Mick looked at him, hope in his face. There was a silence in the morning room, broken only by the scrape of boots on the wooden floor and the hollow sound of a tankard being placed on a table top. Then Sir William suddenly barked out, "But you are forgetting one thing. You are forgetting that Lenehan is a traitor. I have no mercy or compassion for traitors!"

"No!" said Mick sharply. "No, sir! He may have been once, but he is not now."

"Traitors do not change their whole natures in exile," returned Sir William contemptuously. "No one but a fool would suppose it."

"But he was allowed back when the Amnesty was declared. You know that, sir."

Judge Moore remarked that this was indeed true.

"Ah, the Amnesty," scoffed Sir William, dismissing it. "A piece of nonsense to mollify the Whigs. I never approved of it. And anyway, that does not mean, young man, that Lenehan is to be given license to carry on his subversive activities once he is returned. He has been caught red-handed doing so, you know."

Sir William paused, glanced around at the various intent members of his audience, and went on, "There were no less than twoscore muskets and several barrels of powder under his floor when his house was searched, and a printing press as well. Do you regard that as a sign your friend Lenehan has mended his ways?"

Mick said tightly, "You wanted to question him, didn't you?"

The deputy sheriff smoothed the sleeve of his coat. "Perhaps I did."

"You could have put those guns there for your men to find . . ."

"Oh, come," said Judge Moore pacifically, "you are saying more than you mean, Mick."

Sir William's blue eyes had narrowed dangerously. "What in the world are you suggesting?"

Mick said doggedly, "Evidence can be arranged, sir. All the world knows that."

"And you are intimating that I arranged this piece of evidence?"

"William," said Kitty, feeling a need to break in upon their dialogue, if only to say something inane, "do not jump to conclusions. You are as bad as Mick himself, and I really thought you had more sense."

"I would suggest," broke in Judge Moore, evidently feeling an equal need for a diversion before the situation became any uglier, "that we change the subject. If Fossick says that you may not see Lenehan in prison, Mick, you'll just have to accept it as final. And go and put that hot head of yours under the pump, you young rebel," he added, giving Mick's shoulder a shove and steering him toward the door, "or you'll find yourself clapped up in your turn."

There was a general outburst of conversation, with everyone talking at once, and all the assembled gentlemen doing their utmost to overcome any awkwardness that might remain from the unfortunate scene they had witnessed. Mr. Pennefather demanded to know if Sir William had any notion to sell his chestnuts, remarking that he'd seldom seen a finer team. Father James came over to Kitty and asked leave to introduce himself to her, and the only person, indeed, who made no exertion during the next noisy few minutes was Luke.

He was standing, as he had been standing throughout the whole of Mick's encounter with Sir William, leaning his broad shoulders against the wall and apparently taking little interest in what was going on. He had not moved during the whole episode, and did not do so until Kitty began to leave the room.

She found herself face to face with him in the hall. He smiled at her rather grimly and said, "You really cannot avoid meddling in what doesn't concern you, can you? Do you think you have done Mick a service by encouraging him to make a fool of himself?"

"At least I tried to help him. I did not notice that you did anything at all, Mr. Denny."

"No," he agreed. "I saw no point in making a bad matter worse by interfering. But that, I fear, is something your Ladyship could never be made to understand."

"I promised I would ask it of William," she pointed out defensively. "I like to keep my promises, even though I looked even more foolish than your brother."

He smiled at her suddenly, warmly. "Yes, I believe you do," he said, as though the idea was both novel and surprising.

"Is that so odd?" she demanded. "I do not see why gentlemen should have the monopoly of . . . of gentlemanly principles."

"No," he conceded. "But in my experience of females, they are often inclined to be forgetful of their given word, if it suits them. Why should they not, indeed? A pretty face can make up for almost any shortcomings."

"Well, no doubt your experience of females has been rather different from mine," she remarked acidly.

"Naturally. It would be odd, indeed, if it had not been." And when Kitty gave a little choke of laughter at this piece of inanity, he added, "Is Mary keeping you amused?"

"As a matter of fact, Mr. Denny," she told him, "I am pledged to go with Mary to that horrid Castle of yours this afternoon. She wants to ride up there and show it to me in daylight, and if I am leaving tomorrow, as I suppose I must do, this is my last chance. Will your guests think it very uncivil of me if I slip away now without bidding them goodbye?"

"I daresay they'll be looking all over for you," he said, smiling. "And George Dillon will be cast into a melancholy . . ."

"You are being silly, Mr. Denny. Then I may go. . . ?"

"Take Paddy Joe with you, if you do, then," he said. "With those men of Fossick's roaming about, I'd not want you out on your own."

"Do you not realize that those men of Fossick's, as you call them, are here for the purpose of guarding me all the way to Dublin? How shall I be in any danger from them, I should like to know?"

He did not return her smile. "Well, tell Mary that I shall skin her if she tries to escape from Paddy Joe." He did not wait for Kitty to answer, but said immediately, "And promise me one thing, if you wish to oblige me . . ."

"If," she conceded, drawling on the word, "if I wished to oblige you, sir, what then? Do tell me, for who knows when the time may come . . ."

"If you wish to oblige me, ma'am," said Luke coolly, "promise me that you will never try to take a hand in my affairs for my own good. Having seen what your goodhearted meddling has done for Mick, and how nearly Fossick stood in danger of having your Ladyship at the helm of his household, I can really think of no worse a fate than to be the object of one of your . . . er . . . crusades."

He took advantage of her startled and outraged silence, pinching her chin in careless fashion, and went back into the morning room to join the other gentlemen, saying over his shoulder, "Enjoy your ride, ma'am—and give Mary my message."

Kitty and Mary did not take a groom with them. Instead,

they took Shamus and spent a delightful hour wandering around the Castle, with the children tearing up and down the echoing corridors and shouting at each other from the gallery which surrounded the great hall.

She came away with a feeling of sadness for the ruin of what must have once been a lovely house, with its glorious views over the wooded valley. Toward evening they rode down the laurel-crowded avenue, with its weed-matted surface, and mounted the hill over which Luke had led her that first windy night. It all looked very different in daylight. The slopes of the hill changed from lush green to stony, gorse-dotted scree as they neared the top of the pass. The sky was wide and blue, and the wind, though cold, was not as bitter as it had been the day before.

The children were singing as they trotted on ahead to the top of the rise, but their song stopped abruptly when they saw what was below them on the other side of the hill. The lake was spread out between its bowl of hills, ruffled by the sharp wind. On the far side was seen the untidy sprawl of Dennystown House and its outbuildings, with a cluster of thatched cabins straggling down to the lakeside and up the slope behind. On the near side of the water, in a group of trees, the rooftops of Father James's house and the church could be seen. They had been meaning to ride down the gully and into the shelter of these trees, so that there would be no danger of their being observed from Dennystown, but one glance was enough to show them that Father James had visitors.

Sir William Fossick's men were unmistakable, and one look at Shamus's face was enough to convince Kitty that she could not take him to his temporary home while the soldiers were standing about in the graveyard and walking in groups along that part of the lakeshore.

"Come," she said, taking the child's hand, "you may come with Mary and me to the big house, and when those soldiers are once more back at Dennystown, you may slip back without anyone seeing you."

CHAPTER THIRTEEN

JUDGE MOORE and the other gentlemen rode away before long, and only Sir William Fossick and his men were left. Dennystown was oddly quiet that evening. As darkness fell and the candles were lit, the air of tension which had hung about the place all day seemed to intensify. There were sounds of occasional boisterous revelry from the barrack room, it was true, but within the house there was an unmistakable atmosphere of constraint. Luke had decreed that none of the female servants was to leave the house after dark and that the deputy sheriff's men were once again to be given their provisions and then left strictly alone.

Not everyone was aware of the brooding stillness. Mick

was far too busy with his own worries and schemes to notice anything beyond them. He had made up his mind what he had to do. He would get Lenehan out of prison himself, and let them think it was the Green Man. Once the decision was made, a feeling of excitement and anticipation began to build up inside him, and it seemed almost unbearable to have to wait until they had dined and all the household were asleep.

Sir William did not notice anything amiss either. He expected silence while he dressed. He occupied himself with the ticklish task of tying his cravat, and his valet stood beside him in an attitude of reverent attention. The valet had been with Sir William for years and he knew better than to speak or to move while his master wound the long strip of muslin round his neck, dexterously pleating and folding it into place. Once the deputy sheriff had been eased into his dark red coat, a garment which showed off his broad shoulders well, and had put the final touches to his toilette, studying himself carefully from all angles in the mirror, the valet ventured at last to tell Sir William that Sergeant Duffy was waiting to see him.

"He says it's urgent, but I told him that you were dressing." The valet did not at all hold with his master's military underlings, finding them uncouth and vulgar. He had not been sorry to be able to tell the huge, ferocious-looking sergeant that on no account would he be admitted to the master's room until the all-important business of dressing for dinner had been achieved. He asked unctuously, "Shall I tell the sergeant that he may come in, sir?"

"Yes, of course," retorted Sir William irritably. He had been expecting a message from Duffy this past hour or more. "Why the devil didn't you tell me that he was there?"

Sir William strode to the door of his bedroom and flung open the door. He saw the vast, scarlet-coated figure of Duffy standing there, looking oddly ill-at-ease. He told him abruptly to come in and shut the door, at the same time getting rid of the valet by means of one expressive gesture of his hand. "And now," he said, "what have you to tell me? Is all in readiness?"

"It is that, your honor. Not so much as a mouse will be after coming in or out of Dennystown this night without us knowing all about it. And they've sent word from the Castle that it's the same up there."

"Excellent," approved the deputy sheriff. "And you're quite sure your men know what they've to do?"

"They do that, sir."

"And have those left in the barrack room been told to make a deal of noise? If they are too quiet, someone might guess that they are not all there. Let them make as much of a din as they are able."

Sergeant Duffy replied with a hoarse chuckle that there would be no trouble about that. He had seen to it that they had brought a supply of rum in the chaise, and the men were like to have the evening of their lives.

"Well, you may tell those men who are hidden outside that it will be made amply worth their while to miss the revelry," said Sir William, smiling rather unpleasantly. "If we get our man tonight, as I believe we will, there'll be a bag of guineas for each and every one of them. Who has been detailed to follow young Denny until he meets Cullen? Or will you do it yourself?"

The sergeant assured Sir William that he would certainly do it himself, and would make sure that Cullen met young Denny at the prearranged spot.

Sir William nodded his approval, and then said very quietly, "And Duffy, he is to be taken dead or alive, I have said; and between our two selves it might be altogether better if he were to die before he comes up before the judge. If Captain Dillon takes him, and takes him alive, it might be necessary"—the deputy sheriff paused for a moment, and then went on—"it might be necessary to contrive something, Duffy. You follow me?"

Presently he dismissed the sergeant and made his way to the top of the shallow staircase. Looking down the well of the stairs, he saw Mick crossing the hall into the morning room. He drew a deep breath and started slowly down. The evening's entertainment was about to begin. By this time tomorrow the Green Man would be in his hands.

Meanwhile, Kitty would have been only too glad if she had been allowed to dress for dinner in anything like the same reverent silence which had attended the deputy sheriff. But this was not to be, for not only had she to contend with Martha in her most militant mood, but Mary and Shamus were also in the room, fingering her brushes and combs, peering at her dresses where they hung in the great oaken wardrobe, and generally causing a distraction.

Mary had tapped on her door almost as soon as she had gone up to dress. "May we come in, Lady Kitty?" she had asked, beckoning to Shamus and telling him to make haste and shut the door. "Shamus did not like to go out through the yard while those soldiers are still hanging about, so I told him that he could stay with me until they were all safely in their own place. And if you please, ma'am," she concluded breathlessly, "might we come in here until you are all gone into dinner? This is about the only place where he is not likely to be discovered."

Kitty asked rather dryly to be told whether it was Luke that the children were so anxious to avoid, or the soldiers; and Mary, unabashed, said that she would far rather encounter a whole regiment of soldiers than her brother when he was displeased. "He is not always very understanding, you see," she said, grinning.

Kitty laughed. "If it were only you, Miss Mary, I would be tempted to turn you out and leave you to your fate. However, it would be a pity if Shamus were to get into trouble, since it is our fault that he is here. You are both welcome to hide here with me if you think it will save you." She turned about, to see Martha standing in the doorway. "Close the door quickly, Martha dear. We have two fugitives in here."

Martha eyed the two children benignly. "Your supper's waiting for you, Miss Mary," she said, putting a can of hot water down beside the bath. "And who's this?"

"This is Shamus Finn," said Kitty gravely. And as the little boy made his bow with equal gravity, she added, "And both he and Miss Mary are going to help me dress for dinner, so Miss Mary's supper will have to wait."

"Trust your Ladyship to be a bad example," said Martha indulgently as she drew the screen about the copper bath and began to pour water into it. "Well, if you two are going to stay, you will have to sit over there while her Ladyship has her bath. And no fidgeting, mind, or out you'll go!"

As Kitty took her bath, Martha regaled her with a minute-by-minute description of all that had passed in Robert's sick-room since the morning; the medicines he had taken, the restless way in which he had slept, the games that she had invented to keep him happy. His fever was quite gone, Martha assured Kitty. It appeared, also, that whatever doubts Martha had once entertained about Miss Biddy's nursing abilities and the dangerous and unsalubrious nature of Dennystown House, these had for the most part been replaced by a reluctant admiration for Miss Biddy. "Not that I'll not be pleased when we can move him nearer to a doctor, for whatever Miss Biddy may say, I still hold that he should have been cupped while his fever was high." Then she added, "Did you remember to explain to Sir William, milady, that it'd be a day or two before you could move him?"

Kitty had been putting off the moment when she must tell Martha that they were not, after all, going to stay with Sir William. It had been easy enough so far, as Martha had been so full of Robert's illness and there had been nothing for Kitty to do but to listen. But plainly she could put it off no longer.

She turned her back so that her maid could tie the strings of her underdress, and in a calm and unconcerned tone, informed Martha that their visit had been put off. The deputy sheriff, she said, was about to form a very eligible connection with an heiress. Of course, it would never do for him to be entertaining another lady at such a time.

Martha was at first speechless with outrage. This happy state of things did not last, however, and when the floodgates of her wrath were opened, there was no stopping her for some time.

At length Kitty said wearily, "Come, Martha. It is annoying, I know, but since you have predicted disaster from the very outset of our travels, you should be gratified that your fears have been fulfilled."

"I would never have thought it of Sir William, milady! That I would not. I always thought him to be such a sensible, good-hearted sort of man."

"I do not see how you can quarrel with his good sense," drawled Kitty, seating herself before the looking glass and holding out her hairbrush to her maid. "He must be well past thirty, you know, and a man of that age should begin to look around for a wife. And this one is a rich lady, by all accounts."

Martha took the hairbrush in hands that hardly seemed to know what to do with it. "But . . . but to turn your Ladyship

away as if you were nothing . . . no better than a beggar
. . . It's a disgrace, that's what it is!"

"Well, Sir William is doing his best to make amends. He
is sending us to Dublin in his own carriage. And he is even
giving us a military escort, for with his present commitments
at home, he is unable to take us himself . . . That is what the
soldiers are for. They are waiting to take us to Dublin; and
to my mind, the sooner we all leave here, the better." On
these words, Kitty swung round to face Martha. "And we
shall be leaving tomorrow morning. There is to be no argument about it, if you please. We have already trespassed too
long upon Mr. Denny's hospitality . . ."

"Oh, do not go away tomorrow, Lady Kitty!" cried Mary,
bobbing up from her seat at the other end of the room.
"There is so much more that I want to show you, and you are
very welcome to stay here longer! Truly, you are, ma'am!"

"What? Do you still dare to say that I am welcome when
Shamus dare not leave the house for fear of meeting my
escort?" demanded Kitty in a funning tone. "You know very
well that you will be glad to see the last of us all."

"You could send the soldiers away," returned the child.
"You have no need of a guard while you are here."

Kitty smiled. "I know it. It was only when I first set eyes
on those red-coats that I became in any way alarmed. But for
all that, I am determined to leave tomorrow. If Robert is not
well enough to go far," she added, eying Martha coldly, "we
will put up at the first good inn that we come to, and will
remain there until he is better. And now," she added, without giving Martha any time to muster her forces, "we have
more important matters to attend to. Which earrings shall I
wear this evening? Come, Mary. Give me your advice. And
Shamus, also"—smiling at the little boy—"a gentleman's advice is invaluable when it comes to jewelry."

(156)

The contents of Kitty's jewel case were wholly successful in diverting the attention of the children; and although Martha was plainly not won over, she relapsed into a grim silence and proceeded to brush Kitty's short curls without any further verbal outbursts.

The first part of dinner passed by like a dream. Kitty had no recollection afterward as to what she had eaten or what she had drunk, nor even what she had said. She saw the scene with her eyes, but seemed in no way to have participated. It was as if a wall of glass had been put up between herself and the others.

When she thought back upon the evening, she could recall the moving figures of the others like some animated frieze. She could even remember a good deal of what they said, but of her own speech and actions she had no clear recollection. She supposed, afterward, that the strange and unreal events of the past two days must have reduced her to a state of shock, which could account for the apparent vagueness of all that passed.

There was Sir William, immaculately dressed, laughing in his usual loud and merry way at something that had been said, commenting in a somewhat condescending manner upon the quality of the wine, recommending his own wine merchant in Dublin. This Sir William had suddenly become no more than a handsome stranger, and one whose manners, moreover, she could not admire. Miss Biddy had emerged from the sickroom and presided at one end of the polished table, clad in severe black with a monstrous cameo brooch covering her thin chest like a breastplate.

Mick seemed to have entirely regained his usual gaiety of spirits. Indeed, Kitty had never before seen him in such uproarious form. His eyes shone, his face was flushed; yet she noticed that he drank sparingly of his wine and ate little. He seemed to take a naughty delight in sparring with their guest. There was no trace of his previous sullen antagonism, but not one of the deputy sheriff's pronouncements was allowed to pass without an answering quip of some kind.

"How kind of you to let us into your secrets, sir," he remarked after Sir William had finished telling the company that he now employed a French cook, and that their standard of eating at Mount Comeragh Lodge had undergone a complete transformation. He would advise anyone, he said, to follow his example if they had a chance. There was nothing like a Latin when it came to understanding food.

"But are you not a little afraid that you will be accused of harboring one of the enemy?" inquired Mick, winking at Kitty. "French spies are said to be everywhere, you know—and look what happened to Mr. White? Mr. White, Lady Kitty, is a French tutor who gave lessons in the language to some of the Bagwell children, among others, and do you know, he was actually discovered to be in possession of a letter written in the French language? So, naturally, he was immediately apprehended as a spy." Mick turned back to the deputy sheriff, asking solemnly, "Does Judkin Fitzgerald know of this daring step you have taken in changing your cook, sir?"

"Certainly he does," replied Sir William stiffly. "He has even dined with me, and was exceedingly complimentary about the way in which the beef was dressed. And as for the business of White, it was an unfortunate error, I'll not deny it. But as things were at the time, it was also understandable. Fitzgerald regrets that business, I assure you."

"I'm very sure that he does," agreed Mick. "After all, it is not every teacher of French that has such influential friends; and to have chosen to flog that particular one was to a high degree unfortunate."

(158)

"Even the high sheriff can make the occasional mistake."

"Very broad-minded of you, Fossick," applauded Luke gently from his place at the end of the table. He was leaning forward in his chair, cracking a nut.

Kitty, turning her head to look at him, thought she would never forget the way he looked then: his dark head slightly bent, his long-jawed face swarthier than ever in the candlelight, his eyes lowered to the task of cracking a walnut. And his hands, those hands that had held her own when all her world had been shaking, the touch of which had stilled her sense of bewilderment and loss, but whose hard grasp had caused in her a quite different sort of panic, panic both potent and uncontrollable. Uncontrollable was what, in her sensible moments, she knew this feeling could become; and she knew that the only wise course was to get away. For if his touch, and a few lightly spoken words, could cause the very bones to melt in her body; if one kiss could cause such an uproar of emotion, make a slave of her will and send her stumbling from the room like some young and besotted girl, there was really nothing for it but flight. To stay would be madness.

It was for this reason, perhaps, above all the others, that she had resolved to leave Dennystown in the morning. And yet, seeing him there in the candlelight, intent, oblivious of her regard, she thought that she would never recover from the heart-shaking touch of those brown, long-fingered hands. Going away was going to be damnably unpleasant. There would be days and nights when she would long for his touch, for the sight of him, for the sound of his deep, curt voice; but the alternative was madness. It was unthinkable. She might imagine, or wish to imagine, that they shared a sense of the ridiculous, that here was someone she had always known and been waiting for. Of course it was nonsense. There could be no shared life for them, even if he had wished it. Their lives were separate, no point of common interest at all. Besides, she had been on the brink of this particular abyss before, and knew what it was to be drawn down into it, powerless, in love, to be possessed by another in body and mind.

She had been her own mistress now for too long not to realize the value of freedom, and if the price seemed high at times, and if at times she found it lonely, she had no doubt that it was the only way for her. That was why, she supposed, she had seriously thought of marrying William. There would have been no fear of being torn by conflicting emotions, of being forced to laugh when she wished for gravity, of plunging into depths of anguish or soaring to dizzy heights at the merest change of William's humor. No, there would have been no fear of that, she decided, turning to study her erstwhile suitor, but she doubted if she could have borne the tedium.

Mick was saying blithely, "And talking of mistakes, Fossick, have you got any nearer to apprehending the Green Man? I hear you've offered a handsome reward for his capture. A thousand pounds, is it not? That should win some results. Damme, I could do with the money myself!"

"Have you any information to offer me, young man?" inquired Sir William, smiling.

"Do you know," said Mick, momentarily diverted, "you are the second person who has asked me about the Green Man in the last twenty-four hours." He laughed suddenly. "How am I supposed to know about the fellow? I am only just newly returned from Germany. You know, sir," he said with mock earnestness, "I do not think that you can have been pursuing your investigations in the right way. No wonder the Green Man is so highly successful."

Sir William did not look to be in the least put out. Kitty

had, of course, been regaled with several versions of the deputy sheriff's last humiliation at the hands of his enemy, and she could only admire his sangfroid in the face of this blatant teasing. He said, "We shall see. Though the subject is painful to you, I know, I have my hopes that your friend Lenehan will be able to assist me when my men have finished with him tomorrow."

Mick paled visibly at that, and after a moment Sir William turned to Kitty and said, "At what time tomorrow will your Ladyship be ready to set out?"

She had been hoping, perhaps, that Luke would make some suggestion, even ask her to delay her departure. She did not trust herself to look at him, however, and he said nothing. She told Sir William that she would be ready whenever he wished. "But though I am grateful for the loan of your carriage and your horses, William, I am not at all anxious to be marched to Dublin by your horrid soldiers. I shall feel like a prisoner. Indeed, there is no need for them."

"Certainly not," put in Mick. "Besides, sir, how can you spare so many of your crack troops? I thought they were still combing the countryside for Kelagher and his deliverer? Never bother your head about Lady Kitty. I shall escort her to Dublin myself, if she will allow it. But are you really determined to set out tomorrow, ma'am? We had hopes that you were staying longer. Is that not so, Luke?"

Miss Biddy broke in to say in her brisk, matter-of-fact voice, "Little Robert is not fit to travel to Dublin, Lady Katherine. You will be taking a risk if you move him so soon after his fever."

"All the same," retorted Kitty in a voice which sounded high and excitable to her ears, "I am quite set upon leaving in the morning. Pray do not try to dissuade me."

There was a silence. Sir William turned a look of warm

approval upon her. It was the first time, really, that he had looked directly at her since the beginning of dinner. "I think you are very wise to lose no time in setting out, ma'am. And I absolutely assure you that young Robert will take no harm in my carriage. It was specially built for comfort, and is scarcely at all draughty. You may take the journey in easy stages, you know, and my coachman will see to it that you have the very best rooms at Kilkenny and at every other place on the way that you decide to put up. I am well known at all the best houses, and my servants also, and as for your escort, ma'am, it shall be as you wish, of course."

She broke in. "Well, I certainly do not wish to march into a strange inn with twenty red-coats at my heels, William. How ridiculous I should look!"

"They could lodge at the local barracks, ma'am," replied the deputy sheriff earnestly. "You need have no fear of being made conspicuous by my men. They will know just how to go on."

"Oh, will they, indeed?" rejoined Mick in a sarcastic tone. "Then it is a pity, Fossick, that they were not given more careful instructions before coming here. One of them was in a charmingly funning humor this evening, you know, and caused one of the dairymaids to drop her buckets of milk all over the yard. If you have no cream with your morning chocolate, sir, you will know where to lay the blame."

Sir William laughed. "Well, I'll not deny that my men are human, at all events. You cannot blame them if they like a pretty face. Is that why you've imposed your curfew, my dear Denny? I hear that no one is permitted to enter or to leave the house from now on. Is that really the case?"

"A precaution, merely," murmured Luke. "As you say, your men are only human; well, so are mine. And there are some of us who are liable to grow a trifle hasty when our

(162)

women are subjected to too much"—he paused, raising his quizzing glass to look more closely at the deputy sheriff's derisively smiling face—"to too much gallantry, shall we say? So I thought it best to keep my household within doors this evening."

A small silence greeted this remark. Then the moment of quiet was broken by the sound of a scuffle outside the door. A moment later it was flung open and Mary erupted into the room. She paused when she found Luke regarding her coldly through his glass, and dropped a hasty, awkward curtsy. "L . . . Luke," she stammered, "pray will you tell Paddy Joe to stop being so idiotish, and to let Shamus through the door. Father James will be wondering where he is . . ."

Before Luke could answer, Shamus had sidled in through the open door, looking decidedly apprehensive. He was followed by Paddy Joe, whose wrinkled face wore a look of concern.

The groom said gruffly, "Miss Mary wouldn't take no for an answer, Denny. Will you be after telling her that what I said was true?"

"I will indeed, Paddy Joe," said Luke in a voice of ice. "I am only sorry that you have been put to this trouble. I won't keep you any longer." And when the man had nodded, glanced round the room with his sharp little monkey's eyes and left the room, Luke turned toward the shrinking Shamus and said in the same quiet, chill tone, "And why, may I ask, are you here? I told you to stay with Father James, did I not?"

Shamus looked scared and guilty, but he held himself upright, looking Luke in the face with his large eyes.

"Why have you disobeyed me?"

"He did not mean it, Luke," Mary began in a pleading tone. "It was just . . ."

"That will do, Mary," said Luke. "Shamus is no doubt

quite able to make his own excuses. If you have anything to say afterwards, I shall be ready to listen to you. For the moment you will keep quiet."

"But . . ."

"Either keep quiet or leave the room. Which is it to be?"

Kitty had been observing this encounter between Luke and her young friends with some amusement. Mary appeared, for once, to be thoroughly abashed. She subsided into a blushing silence.

Kitty turned to see whether Sir William was equally diverted by this unorthodox and unscheduled entertainment, and saw a look of such horror upon his face that she almost gasped. For the deputy sheriff was sitting forward in his chair, his hands clenched into fists, his face blotched, drained of its normal high color. He was gazing at Shamus for all the world as if he were seeing a ghost. As Kitty continued to stare at him, puzzled, the ruddy color began to run back into his face, and with a hand that palpably shook, Sir William reached for his glass and took a hurried draught of wine.

Meanwhile Shamus was embarking upon a stumbling explanation of his reasons for being where he was, and was making a poor job of it. "I just came for a minute or two," he said. "I . . . I was riding with Mary and . . ." He paused again and cast an agonized look in Kitty's direction. "And also with her Ladyship," he concluded unhappily.

His look of misery was too much for Kitty. After all, it had been she who had invited him in, since at the time he had appeared far too terror-stricken to be sent off round the lake on his own. Wondering whether she, too, was inviting a blistering setdown by coming to Shamus's aid, she said, "Mr. Denny." He turned his head and looked at her very directly. "I have a confession to make. I invited him to come in, so if anyone is to blame, it is myself."

(164)

Luke went on looking at her for a moment without speaking. A glint of laughter lit his eyes. "I should have known it," he said at length. "What other trouble will you plunge us into, I wonder, before you leave in the morning?"

Torn between disappointment that he should take her departure as a decided thing and joy at the now familiar upsurge of amusement, she said in a stifled voice, "If you will only forgive Shamus, Mr. Denny, I will undertake to behave unexceptionably until I go."

"I wonder if you really could manage it?"

She said demurely, "Well, I do think you might give me a chance, sir."

He raised his brows, mocking her. Then, abruptly, he returned his attention to the children. "You had better go to bed," he said. "Shamus, you will sleep in my room tonight, and you will go back to Father in the morning. Now go!"

Shamus turned to go. For Mary, however, this was almost too much of an anticlimax. She said, "Why can Shamus not sleep in his own room? His bed is still ready for him, you know."

Luke got to his feet with a suddenness that made her take a hasty step backward, and without a word he took her by the shoulder and propelled her through the door, closing it with a snap. Sir William had also, for some reason, risen to his feet.

Luke strolled back toward the dining table, eying his guest with some amusement. "You recognize young Shamus, I see, Fossick. He is very like his mother, is he not?"

Sir William shook his head wordlessly. Then he nodded, swallowed something which seemed to have got stuck in his throat, and said hoarsely, "What is that boy doing here? What is he to you, may I ask?" He looked around him, saw that every person in the room was regarding him with expressions ranging from curiosity to a sort of malicious enjoyment,

(165)

and said in a more controlled tone, "I never thought to see that child again. I thought . . . I thought he had perished in the fire with his mother and the old Finns."

"Fortunately," replied Luke, helping himself to a pinch of snuff, "fortunately he escaped. But as a result of his experiences he has a lively terror of soldiers and of all things military. That was why I sent him over to the priest's house while you were here with your men, Fossick."

"And that is why he is still in this house," put in Kitty. "So do not scold him, Mr. Denny. He was positively frozen with horror at the sight of William's men, and I had not the heart to send him away alone. Really, William, it was too bad of you."

Sir William said acidly, "If I had known I should cause so much consternation, ma'am, or even," he added pointedly, "had I been aware that poor Katie Finn's bastard was being kept here, I might have taken more pains to keep my men out of the way."

Mick said, rather maliciously, "You do not appear to be overjoyed to find him alive, at all events?"

"Why should I be?" retorted Sir William. "The child may live or die, for all I care. However, since he is alive, you are welcome to him."

"For shame, William!" cried Kitty. "He is the dearest little boy."

Sir William shrugged his shoulders and said with studied arrogance, "You are welcome to your opinion, ma'am. For my part, I should hesitate before giving a home to a child who was born in a Dublin back slum, to a woman of exceedingly doubtful morals . . ." He paused, and before Kitty could voice her indignation at such a heartless speech, he added, "But doubtless Denny has his reasons for doing so."

Kitty had been under the impression that Sir William had

meant his last remark to be taken as a rhetorical question, but Luke chose to answer him literally. "Why, yes," he murmured, looking quite maddeningly sure of himself. "Why, yes, my dear Fossick. I have my reasons. Remind me to tell you what they are some day."

Sir William looked blankly at his host, as though he suspected some deeper meaning but could not tell what it was. Then he shrugged his shoulders once again, saying coldly, "I doubt if I should be interested, Denny. The Finn female was a good-looking wench, and I was as shocked as any at the manner of her death, but as for her bastard child, you are welcome to do what you like with him."

"Thank you, Fossick," replied Luke blandly. "That is precisely what I mean to do."

CHAPTER FOURTEEN

CULLEN WAS WAITING for Mick at the edge of the town. He seemed uneasy. He said sharply, "Did you know that Denny went through the town tonight?"

Mick stared at him incredulously in the gloom. "Impossible!"

" 'Tis true, Mister Mick. Himself it was, for I saw him plain. He rode by me at a sharp trot, and he'd got that little Finn lad up in front of him. I don't like it, Mister Mick. It don't make sense . . ."

"It certainly does not," said Mick soberly. "And if you are right, I wonder how he got out of Dennystown. I had the devil's own job getting out myself, what with Luke setting guards over all the inner doors and the fear of meeting any of the deputy sheriff's fellows . . ." Mick sounded quite weary, and a moment later he added impatiently, "But let's get on with our own business, Cullen. If we waste more time finding reasons for Luke, it'll be dawn and too late to help Lenehan."

In the prison, all was in readiness. Captain Dillon found himself wishing for the tenth time that there was light enough in the prison for him to see his watch. But the darkness was total. He seemed to have been mewed up in the evil-smelling, airless place for hours, entombed there with that groaning old man in the next cell for his only company.

Lenehan was not his only company, of course, for there were a dozen men secreted nearby. They were so quiet (Dillon had picked them carefully) that one could almost believe that they were not there.

Captain Dillon had wondered several times during the evening whether Fossick had run mad. The deputy sheriff was certainly more than a little unbalanced on the subject of his enemy and tormentor, and why he should have got this idea into his head that the Green Man should choose to rescue Lenehan on this very night, Captain Dillon had no notion. He had his orders and he meant to obey them. There was a chance that Fossick did not know what he was about, and although Captain Dillon did not like him, he had a respect for his efficiency. There had been an impressive air of certainty about him when he had foretold the Green Man's attempt.

A dozen men would be enough, Sir William had assured him. All they had to do was to hide themselves around Lenehan's cell and await developments. The Green Man would come at any time between two and four in the morning and would attempt to take Lenehan out of prison. After that, Sir William had remarked dryly, Captain Dillon might use his own initiative; but the villain was to be taken, dead or alive, and put in irons.

Captain Dillon had come into the prison as soon as it was dark, bringing with him a dozen of his hand-picked, most disciplined men. They were very different from the majority of troops in the Clonmel garrison. The captain had seen service in America and India, and was by no means one of the rich, idle sort of officer so numerous at that time.

The situation in the county was frankly distasteful to him. It seemed that there were hardly any wholly uncorrupt or professional soldiers among his brother officers, and since the late rebellion, almost any kind of troops were used to keep the countryside in subjection. Many of them were Hessian mercenaries, whose methods were brutal and savage, and the officers did little to restrain their licentious behavior.

There were some pretty ugly tales told about Sir William Fossick's men, too, and for all that Captain Dillon and his few closer friends might joke about Fossick's army, he did not feel at all easy in his mind about them ranging around at Dennystown. Still less did he think them an appropriate escort for Lady Kitty Harcombe, and if there had been time he might have protested to Fossick about it. Captain Dillon hoped with all his might that he would soon manage to get recalled to England. He wanted nothing more than to escape from the hate-torn country that he was in and to reach comparative sanity again.

When he first took up his stance in the prison, however, it had been in no spirit of boredom or disgust. He was frankly excited and was looking forward to the night's events. But time went by, and it was dank and cold in his hiding place, and eventually he came to wondering whether Fossick had been mistaken. Perhaps the earnest deputy sheriff had been the victim of some practical joker.

At long last, however, when he was half paralyzed with boredom and cold, a new sound came to his ears. A tingle of excitement ran through his chilled limbs and he drew in a quiet breath. He listened tensely. Someone was coming stealthily down the stone-flagged passage. It was just as Fossick had foretold. He was not even being particularly quiet. If it was indeed the Green Man, the fellow seemed pretty sure of himself, for as he groped his way into Lenehan's cell the captain heard him whisper the prisoner's name.

Lenehan groaned aloud. "Ah, leave me be, sir. I'm not after knowing nothing, as the Holy Saints can witness."

"Shh!" The captain heard more whispers, and then came a soft exclamation as Lenehan's chains rattled against the stone floor.

"That's right, sir. They've chained me up like a dog."

"The devil they have!"

There was another vigorous clanking of chains, and Captain Dillon strained his ears for another sound of that voice. He could hardly credit it, but it sounded like Mick Denny. It was not possible! Why, he'd seen him only an hour or two since!

"Look, John," said Mick quite clearly and unmistakably, "I'll go and get a file or something, and I'll be back as soon as may be . . ."

At that moment Captain Dillon stepped noiselessly out of his hiding place and said, "I think not. You will stay where you are."

There was a gasp from Mick and a moan from the old man. Behind him the captain heard the scrape of flints as the two men with orders to do so set about lighting their lanterns. And then as the first gleam of light showed him Mick's startled face, the young man pulled out a pistol and stood in front of Lenehan, his eyes blazing and his teeth tightly set. "If you come nearer, I'll shoot."

"Now, Mick," said the captain in a firm and reasoning tone, "show your good sense by giving yourself up quietly."

"If you'll let this old man go free, I'll do as you ask!"

"I can't do that."

Mick's dazzled eyes had grown more accustomed to the sudden light which had appeared over his captor's shoulder. He said in a more normal tone, "Good God, George! It's you, is it! What the deuce are you doing here at this hour of night?"

"I might ask the same of you."

Mick laughed a trifle hysterically. "So you might. Well, let John go and I'll tell you."

"No. Don't tell me," said the captain wearily. Truth to tell, he was feeling sick at heart. It was one thing to set a trap for the Green Man, but quite another to find that the man he had laid in wait for was one of his friends. "You may say anything you have to say to Fossick in the morning."

"Fossick?" Mick sounded truly dismayed. "You don't mean to haul me in front of him, do you? Damn it, George, this is only a jest! Or it would be," he added as Lenehan coughed rackingly at his feet, "if it were not for John."

"If you can convince Fossick that it is only a jest, I shall be only too pleased. Meanwhile, though, put that pistol down. You may shoot me if you've a mind to, but there are twelve men behind me and you cannot shoot them all."

"Damn you, George, get out of my way! If you think I'm going to all this trouble to get John out of Fossick's clutches, and then give him up to you without making a fight for it, you've got windmills in your head!"

"You've no choice in the matter."

Mick glared at his friend, beginning to realize in that moment the hopelessness of his position, and then he said recklessly, "All right, George. But you'll have to take me, you know. Come and do it, if you can."

The captain hesitated for only a couple of seconds. Then he walked forward slowly, his own more serviceable-looking pistol leveled at Mick's chest, keeping his eyes locked to

Mick's. He saw the young man's glance flick toward the door, and took his chance. Mick gasped, saw too late that he had lost his advantage, and pulled the trigger. But it was too late. Perhaps Mick never meant to shoot straight. There was a deafening report and the ball whistled harmlessly past the captain's head, and then the two men were struggling together on the hard stone floor, the captain's pistol scuttering away behind him as they wrestled, grunting and gasping, for supremacy.

It was actually Lenehan's shackles which brought about Mick's defeat, for he somehow got one of them tangled round his elbow, and before he could win free he was pinned to the ground.

"Give me your word that you'll behave," panted the captain, "and I won't have you put in irons." But the only answer he got to this merciful offer was an exceedingly rude comment upon his genealogy. "Oh, very well," he said resignedly, "have it the hard way, if you wish." He watched as two of his men seized Mick and dragged him into the adjoining cell, where leg-shackles were already chained to the wall. Sir William had given strict instructions that the Green Man was to be put in irons, and with Mick being so intransigent, there seemed to be no way out of it.

When he was made fast, Captain Dillon went in to him. "I'll have your blood for this, George! See if I don't! I thought you were one of my friends!" Mick said through clenched teeth.

The captain did not answer for a moment or two. Then he said, "I wish it were anyone but you. But you see, don't you"—almost as if he were pleading with his captive—"that I have absolutely no choice in the matter? I don't say that I have not admired some of the things you've done, but even I cannot approve of all of them. Kelagher was a murderer. He was convicted in a court of law. You were very wrong to take his part."

"Kelagher?" echoed Mick. "What has he to do with John Lenehan?"

The captain sounded weary. "Do not try to persuade me that you had nothing to do with him, I'd as soon you did not lie to me. And besides, they found that chest in the Castle with some of Kelagher's clothes in it, and the hangman has identified that mask as his own."

Mick looked not so much guilty as utterly dumbfounded. his mouth fell open. "B . . . but . . ."

"And do not start to protest your innocence to me," said the captain testily. "I am trying to help you. So listen carefully to what I have to say . . ."

"But look here," said Mick desperately. "It was all part of the jest to make you think I was the Green Man, but you don't really believe it, do you?"

"I cannot help but believe it," said Captain Dillon sadly. "And anyway, it does not matter what I believe. It is Fossick you will have to convince. He will be in to see you in the morning, and I fear he means to get you hanged." For the first time Captain Dillon saw a flicker of fear in Mick's eyes. "I'll tell you what," he said. "I'll ride to Dennystown and speak with your brother. If anyone can help you, he can."

"He'd be more inclined to murder me instead," retorted Mick with a wry grin. "But I'd be obliged to you, George, if you'd tell him. God knows what trumped-up tale Fossick will give him."

"Now, Mick," said the captain, not unkindly, "there's only one thing you can do, and that's to tell Fossick everything he wants to know. If you make a full confession and give Kelagher up, you may stand a chance of getting off lightly. I daresay you know it well enough, but you're a damned popular figure in the county and you have admirers in surprising places. Except for Fossick, I don't suppose people will want to see you hang. At least, they wouldn't have done before you went beyond the pale in abducting a convicted murderer."

Mick simply gaped at the captain, apparently bereft of speech, and his captor thought that he might as well hammer home his advice. "Give them Kelagher, Mick, and you may not do so badly after all."

And with this last piece of counsel, he turned on his heel, leaving Mick alone with his chaotic thoughts.

CHAPTER FIFTEEN

"YOU HAVE PUT HIM IN IRONS, I trust," said Sir William.

"Yes, sir."

"Then I suppose he will be safe enough," the deputy sheriff conceded somewhat grudgingly. "But really, Dillon, you could have just as well sent word by one of your men."

Captain Dillon eyed the deputy sheriff unenthusiastically and said, "I preferred to bring it myself."

Sir William was displeased. He had been awaiting the news of Mick's arrest with some eagerness, but the sight of Captain Dillon's pink, good-natured face had caused him a distinct qualm of annoyance. He did not want Captain Dillon hanging about Dennystown that morning. He wondered how best to get rid of the fellow. He was sure that the Green

Man's identity had been a shock to the captain, and it might even prove entertaining to see how he reacted to seeing Denny brought to this pass. But after that, it would be better, very much better, if the well-meaning captain could be removed.

He saw that the captain was looking past him in a somewhat embarrassed fashion, and turned to see Luke coming toward them, strolling across the stable yard with a spaniel at his heels as though he had not a care in the world. Sir William had, in a manner of speaking, been waiting for this moment for a number of years. He bowed to his host with rather more than his usual grace and said suavely, "Good morning, Denny. A fine morning, is it not?"

Luke nodded civilly enough, but turned to survey the captain with an expression of mild astonishment. "Well, George? Is this a social visit? You look a trifle heavy-eyed, if you'll forgive my saying so."

"No, Denny," said the captain awkwardly, "it's not a social visit, I'm afraid. Fossick'll tell you, though."

"Fossick does appear to be rather pregnant with tidings, doesn't he? But shall we eat something first?"

"What I have to tell you, Denny, will scarcely increase your appetite," said Sir William.

"It's as bad as that, is it?" Luke raised his eyeglass and surveyed the deputy sheriff. "Then by all means let us eat first." But when Sir William did not stir from his determined stance in front of the open door, Luke sighed gently and said, "I see there is no holding you. What is it, then?"

"It concerns your brother, Denny."

"Oh, it does, does it?" returned Luke cheerfully. "What has Mick been about?"

"Laugh if you wish, Denny, but your brother will be lucky if he does not hang before the week's out. He's in Clonmel, under close arrest, and will have to stand his trial for treason."

Luke was no longer smiling. His long, dark face looked, indeed, somewhat grim. "In what kind of treasonable activity has Mick been involved?"

"He tried to take Lenehan from prison last night."

"Is that treason? I would call it foolishness, certainly, but scarcely treasonable."

"That is not all, Denny. Feign ignorance if you must, but I warn you that I mean to bring you to book as an accessory to your brother's crimes. While you assume that look of innocence, however, I suppose I shall have to humor you. In plain words, then: Mick is the Green Man. He has pulled the wool over our eyes for long enough, but last night he gave himself away finely. He is the Green Man all right. And as soon as he's obliging enough to tell us where he's hidden Kelagher, we'll string them both up on Kilnabawn Bridge."

"What a bloodthirsty creature you are, Fossick," murmured Luke, his tight mouth lifting at one corner. "But what in the world made you think that Mick was the Green Man? He was in Germany until a mere six weeks ago."

"Nonsense!" retorted Sir William loudly. "He was no more in Germany than I was myself."

"Oh, but he was," replied Luke calmly, helping himself to snuff, "and it can be proved that he was."

"How, pray?"

"By sending to Germany, of course."

"Ah!" The deputy sheriff was smiling unpleasantly. "Do you hope to delay the trial on the pretext of sending for witnesses? Believe me, Denny, we are not all such fools as you think. Mick will be brought to trial as soon as may be, and if he is wise he will tell us where Kelagher is hiding."

"He knows nothing of Kelagher."

Sir William raised his eyebrows. "The recapture of Kelagher is a matter of urgency, Denny. Mick will be very wise to give us help. If he does not, then I am very much afraid that he will get hurt."

"If he is hurt," said Luke softly and deliberately, "then you will have reason to be afraid, Fossick."

There was a short silence while the two tall men eyed each other.

Captain Dillon said uncertainly, "Oh, don't let us lose our sense of proportion, gentlemen. Fossick did not mean what you thought, Denny. We are not living in the days of the Spanish Inquisition, you know."

"You relieve me," said Luke dryly. "And now, Fossick, unless you have any more to say, may we go into the house?"

This time Sir William made no attempt to prevent them, and they passed into the hallway, then into the little book-room, where a mobcapped maid was lighting the fire. Luke dismissed her and said, "What is all this to do with you, George?"

Sir William replied before the captain could do so. "Why, he had the honor of clapping the Green Man in irons, that's what he had to do with it."

"There was no help for it, Denny. I'm sorry, but there was no other way of restraining him. I tried to make him give me his word not to escape, but he was violent . . ." The captain shook his head in a weary way. "If you could speak to him, Denny, you may be able to calm him."

"A spell in irons will calm him, no doubt," said Sir William, who was warming the back of his legs at the fire. "Denny is certainly not going near him. He's as deep in this business as young Mick, and you need not think, Dillon, that I'm giving them a chance to put their heads together before the trial."

"Sir!" protested Captain Dillon in dismay and disbelief. "You are not serious? Such a thing is . . . impossible . . ."

"You are entitled to your opinion, of course, but for my part I cannot believe that Denny can have been ignorant of young Mick's nefarious activities. He could never have carried on the deception for so long."

"I agree," said Luke. "He could not have done so."

"Well, then . . ."

"Nor did he do so. Mick has done none of the things of which you propose to accuse him, Fossick, except for last night's foolishness. That," Luke added in a mildly derisive tone, "was a neat little trap, Fossick."

Sir William looked momentarily nonplused. Then he gave the tails of his coat a small flip and said, "You cannot blame me for trying to trap the notorious Green Man, can you, Denny?"

"I doubt if you would have succeeded in trapping anyone except my excitable, credulous brother," returned Luke, "but then, it was he you wanted, wasn't it? Well, you will make a fool of yourself, you know."

"Don't think to bluff your way out of this, Denny. We are not all fools."

"I never thought you a fool, Fossock, though I know you to be a knave."

"You'll not help your brother by being insulting."

Captain Dillon said tentatively, "Would Denny be permitted to visit Mick if I were to take him, and undertook to remain with them during their interview?"

Sir William said curtly, "Certainly not. Denny will not be leaving here until the day of the trial. I'm not having him running all about the county canvassing sympathy and support for himself and his brother, upturning the course of justice with his blandishing ways . . ."

"The course of . . . what, Fossick?"

"The course of justice," repeated Sir William, secure in his position of authority and determined to be unmoved by

Denny's barbs. "No one will leave Dennystown from now on —not you, nor any member of your household, Denny. My men will see to it, and they are already calling all your people together so that I may apprise them of my wishes. Sergeant Duffy will be in command here, and if you are wise, you will give Duffy no trouble. Duffy is a man of somewhat slow understanding, but he always obeys my orders to the letter. He has been told to keep you here, at whatever cost."

Captain Dillon knew something of Sergeant Duffy's reputation, and he broke in to say, "I'll stay here myself, if you wish, sir."

"No," replied the deputy sheriff flatly. But he was not quite as quelling as he might have been, for it had suddenly occurred to him that Captain Dillon might be removed in a quite simple and natural way. Captain Dillon should have the honor of escorting Lady Kitty to Dublin. It would keep him out of the way for at least a week. He told the captain of what he had in store for him, explaining that his men would be occupied at Dennystown and would therefore be unable to take the widow to her destination.

"What a signal honor, George, to be considered fair exchange for twenty men," marveled Luke softly. "She will no longer need to fear the safety of her jewel box, at all events."

"My men would have escorted her Ladyship perfectly properly," said Sir William. "You need not try to insinuate anything to the contrary, Denny."

"Oh, I know that," returned Luke cordially. "There is no need to insinuate anything when your . . . army's reputation is so well known in the county."

"If you are sensible, Denny, you will keep a civil tongue in your head. You are in no position to cross swords with me."

"That must explain why you are looking so uncommonly pleased with yourself, Fossick. Last time we crossed swords, if I remember . . ."

"Enough!" hissed Sir William, exasperated out of his well-maintained calm. "Dillon, tell the men who are in the hall that I wish to see them. I have no more time to waste."

PRESENTLY CAPTAIN DILLON FOUND himself in the servants' hall. There were a good many people there, and as the captain came in at one end, he saw Sergeant Duffy marching in at the other, shepherding Paddy Joe and one of his lads from the stable. Paddy Joe was demanding to know what was the matter. His voice shook a little. The captain went over and greeted him.

"Ah, 'tis you, Captain!" exclaimed the old man. "I never thought to see the day when the likes of them"—he shook his head in the direction of two of the red-coats—"were walking in and out as though they owned the place. 'Twas a bad day for us when Himself brought that lady here, and that's a fact. He'd have done better to have left her alone; and the quicker she's gone, the better. Then we'll be free of the sheriff's divils."

The captain had no time to tell him of the emptiness of this hope, for at that moment the deputy sheriff came in with Luke and a couple of militiamen. Luke's shoulders were hunched in an uncomfortable way, and as he turned, manhandled by his guards, his hands were seen to be tied.

"Put him over there, in the corner, and keep him there," commanded Sir William; and as they half pushed, half led Luke to the farthest part of the servants' hall, he continued, "Now, Duffy, is everyone here? I want them here at once. With the exception of the lady in the west wing, of course. You will see to it that she does not leave her room until Captain Dillon removes her."

Sergeant Duffy said that this had been seen to. There were still a few more of the household to be rounded up.

Paddy Joe said in a quiet voice, "If you'd rung the bell, sir, you'd not have needed to hunt us all out."

"Mind your own business, you old dotard," said Sir William contemptuously, "From now on I am master here, and I shall do as I please."

"There's only one master of Dennystown," replied the old man with dignity, "and that's Himself, for all you've tied him up."

"Paddy," said Luke warningly from his place at the back of the room, "Sir William is in charge here for the moment."

"Thank you, Denny," said Sir William acidly, "but I am perfectly able to maintain order here without your assistance."

Captain Dillon turned to Sir William and said in an under-voice, "Have you remembered, sir, that tonight is Lord Comeragh's ball? Will you not be obliged to leave very soon?"

"Presently, Captain," replied Sir William. "All in good time."

The servants had by then been herded into the hall, some looking scared and flustered, some merely curious. Miss Biddy came in, leading Mary by the hand. Miss Biddy looked anything but pleased, but catching Luke's eye and receiving a nod from him, she allowed herself to be led to a chair beside Sir William. She gave him a cold, composed look, but said nothing. In a few more minutes the room was full of whispering, curious, frightened people, and the sergeant told Sir William that all were now assembled.

"But this is not all," the deputy sheriff said. "Where is the boy?"

No one spoke, but there was a rustle of apprehension in the ranks. Miss Biddy turned her head in its neatly starched cap and stared at Sir William.

"Well?" he demanded. "Where is he?"

Miss Biddy said, "Which boy do you mean, Sir William?"

"Why, Katie Finn's bastard, of course," he retorted, very much at his ease. "That red-haired brat who burst in upon us last evening. I've a notion to take him with me to Mount Comeragh Lodge as a hostage—a form of security for your good behavior here, shall we say?"

"He is not here," said Luke. "Katie Finn's child is no concern of yours, Fossick."

"I mean to take him with me."

"You cannot. He is gone."

There was a momentary pause and a movement of astonishment in some quarters, for young Shamus had certainly been gallivanting about the house on the previous evening. Sir William's fair skin took on a more ruddy hue than was usual to it, and he told the soldiers to bring Luke before him. "He must be here," he said evenly enough. "You may not have been aware of it, Denny, but every door to this house, and every window, was being watched last night. No one left except that rascally brother of yours."

Sergeant Duffy's rumbling voice was heard, assuring the deputy sheriff that it had not been possible for the lad to escape in the night.

"I had him removed," said Luke.

"I don't believe you."

"I give you my word, Fossick."

"The word of a rebel, Denny?" scoffed Sir William. "Why should you have removed him?"

"I might ask you what you want of him," replied Luke curtly.

"He'll be better off with me than in this den of papists and traitors," retorted Sir William. There was a quickly stifled hiss of anger throughout the room. Perhaps it died so suddenly because the cold blue eyes of the deputy sheriff swept over the company, or perhaps it was due to the way that Luke turned his dark head slightly and raised his brows. Only Paddy Joe broke into speech, tempestuously, his elderly voice shaking more than ever. "If Himself was not tied fast, sir, you'd not speak to his face like that!"

Sir William and Luke ignored this outburst. Luke said gravely, "Find yourself another hostage, Fossick."

Sir William was inwardly seething with impatience and frustration. He had not much time to find the boy, but he was determined to do so. He could not have left the house last night; it was not possible. Perhaps if Denny were absent, one of his household might give the boy up. "Rourke!" he said curtly. One of the militiamen stepped forward. "Take Denny down to the wine cellar and shut him up. And don't bother to untie his hands."

"Really, Sir William!" protested Miss Biddy, no longer able to contain herself. "If my nephew tells you that Shamus is not here, he will not be here."

"Have you a fancy for the wine cellar, ma'am? No? Then sit down and keep a still tongue in your head."

"Luke would not lie," said Mary in her clear little voice. "He never does."

"Be silent!" thundered the deputy sheriff. Mary flinched backward as though he had struck her, clinging to Paddy Joe, who was beside her. The head lad put his arm around her. Sir William smiled. "You are afraid of me, are you, my dear? Well, you need not be, if you'll only tell me where they've hidden young Shamus. You'll know where to find him, I'll be bound."

Mary shook her head, speechless with fright. Captain Dillon said sharply and anxiously, "Sir! Remember, she is only a child."

"And all the more likely to know where the other child is, don't you think?" returned Sir William, still smiling.

"Sir," said the captain imploringly, "you have Denny's word that the boy is gone."

"My dear Dillon," said Sir William irritably, "Denny may give himself airs and think himself first cousin to God, but believe me, he's no different from the rest of these bog papists. They can all bend the truth to suit themselves. No!" he ejaculated savagely. "The boy must be here somewhere, and I mean to find him." He turned with slow deliberation toward Mary, "And Miss Mary is going to help me in my search . . ."

"No!" cried the little girl, "I cannot . . ."

Both Captain Dillon and Miss Biddy started to say something, but Sir William sharply ordered them to be silent. "Captain Dillon, I believe we can dispense with your presence. There is nothing more for you to do here. Go and see her Ladyship, and render her any help she may need."

The captain said in a low voice, "Pray let me stay, sir."

"Go, Captain Dillon," repeated the deputy sheriff, dangerously precise in the way he enunciated the words. The captain still seemed to hesitate, and Sir William added, "I have no intention of hurting the child. It will not be necessary, I assure you . . ."

Sir William watched calmly as the captain made his departure. The rest of the Denny household saw him go, too, feeling that their last friend and protector had been taken from them. "Now," said Sir William, turning back to look at Mary, "where is Shamus Finn? The sooner you tell me, the better."

Mary had been sheltering in the circle of Paddy Joe's arm. However, she had by now recovered from her first spasm of overwhelming terror, and she came a little way toward him and said reproachfully, "I told you, sir. I don't know where he is. He went away while I was sleeping." She met Sir William's cold blue gaze and fear gripped her again. She said

(186)

in a scarcely audible whisper, shaking her head in desperate denial, that she did not know. Truly, she did not.

"We shall have to use our powers of persuasion, I see," said Sir William; and as Mary drew back, her plain bony face stiff with fright, he said sharply to Sergeant Duffy, "Take the old man and truss him up."

Then Mary's nightmare began in earnest. She saw Paddy Joe's gnarled hands being tied behind his back, and saw him hauled bodily to the place where the sergeant was waiting for him. Only when Sergeant Duffy looked down at the old man with a smile of anticipation did anyone speak. Miss Biddy said sharply, "Have a care what you are about, sir! He is an old man."

"Now, Miss Biddy," said Paddy Joe, peering at Miss Biddy with his lively monkey's eyes, "don't be bothering your head. I've no notion where that young varmint might be, and I'd not be telling the gentleman if I had." In his faded livery, which looked to have been made for a far stouter man, Paddy Joe might well have been thought a figure of fun. No one felt like laughing, however. Even Sergeant Duffy stopped showing his blackened teeth and made a rumbling sound in his throat.

"Now," said Sir William, turning to Mary once again, "where is Shamus? If you don't want the old man to be hurt, you'll tell me quickly."

Mary screamed that she did not know, then burst into hysterical sobs, holding her clenched hands to her mouth.

"Keep her quiet, can't you?" Sir William ordered Miss Biddy. Miss Biddy got up at once and held the shuddering, terror-racked child against her chest so that she could not see what was going on. This did not please the deputy sheriff, for he abruptly ordered her to turn the child round. "I want her to watch, and perhaps she may change her mind about how much she knows."

"Sir William!" It seemed that Miss Biddy was going to defy him, but as he stepped toward her, she capitulated and coaxed Mary to sit upon her knee, facing Paddy Joe and the sergeant.

Sir William might have been at a social gathering, to judge from the ease and affability of his manner. He nodded to the huge sergeant and remarked to the assembled company, in the manner of one who speaks of a favorite dog who is about to perform some feat, "Duffy's strength, you know, is really something out of the common way. I have seen him lift a boulder and carry it out of the path of my carriage; and I have seen him hang a man with his bare hands . . ." He glanced round the room. "Or half hang a man, which is sometimes more . . . effective . . ." He nodded to the sergeant. "We shall see."

The sergeant put his huge hands round Paddy Joe's scrawny neck. The great sinewy fingers tightened their hold, and slowly, as though Paddy Joe had been as light as a rag doll, he swung the old man off the floor and held him kicking and dangling before him. Mary screamed again and tore herself from Miss Biddy's slackened grasp, running toward the sergeant and his gurgling prey. Sir William caught her, however, dragging her back by the hair and slapping her tear-wet face sharply with his other hand. Above the clamor of protest and distress, and the dreadful sounds which were coming from the stifling head lad, he roared down at her, "Tell me where the boy is! Tell me now!"

But Mary was past speech, past coherent thought, and a second or two later it became apparent that it was too late for anybody's words to save Paddy Joe. Perhaps the sergeant had misjudged the strength of his hands, or perhaps the old man's struggles were his undoing. There was a dull crack: Paddy Joe's neck was broken. It was a minute before the sergeant seemed to be aware of it, and then, with a look of dawning astonishment, he lowered the twitching body to the ground and stood looking down, his great hands hanging at his side.

Sir William let Mary go. He did not seem to notice as Miss Biddy swooped over and gathered the child into her arms; he saw only Sergeant Duffy, who was standing gazing at the body of his victim with a look of surprise and disappointment, for all the world like a child who has just knocked down a castle of bricks.

Sir William had a momentary vision of disaster and ruin. It had been no part of his plan to let the old man die. Duffy had performed his grisly act of half-hanging half a dozen times and never killed his victim yet. And in this lay its efficacy, for people would betray their own mothers rather than face another dose of that medicine. But Paddy Joe was undoubtedly dead, and with the eyes of the silent, accusing throng of Denny's dependents fastened upon his face, Sir William was for a moment at a loss.

But he was not the man to give way to his fears, however strong. Pulling himself together, he said, "Careless of you, Sergeant. But don't just stand there. You might have spared yourself some trouble if you'd got the old man to talk. Now you will have to find the boy. Get Matthews to take the old man's body over to the priest, and he'd better stay there and keep the priest from meddling up here. And you will start to look for the boy now. When you've found him you'll bring him to me at Mount Comeragh Lodge. Turn the house inside out. I want that boy."

"William Fossick," said Miss Biddy quietly, "you will regret this morning's work."

He might, for all the notice he took, have been deaf to Miss Biddy's sternly spoken reproof. He gave orders that all the household were to be put down in the main cellar. "We'll leave Denny to his wine casks. It will do him no harm to be parted from his adherents."

"WILLIAM!" exclaimed Kitty indignantly when the deputy sheriff appeared at the door of her bedchamber. "What in the world is going on? First of all I am positively imprisoned in my rooms and someone must have done away with Martha, for I found Robert all alone and had to bring him in here."

She did not tell him that she had found Robert asleep, clutching a sheet of paper in his hot little hand. It had been a note from Luke. It told her that Mick was in trouble. If she wished to help him, it said, she must leave Dennystown directly the deputy sheriff came for her. She had the note buttoned inside the bodice of her traveling dress at that moment, and its stiff edges were a tangible reminder that she must do as Luke requested her. It was not easy. Nor was it easy to maintain her light-hearted manner.

"What is the matter, William?" she demanded, trying to smile. "Are the French landing, or some such thing?"

"Not quite that," murmured Sir William, looking across at Captain Dillon, who was standing glumly by the window, "but something of a crisis, for all that. Did not Dillon enlighten you?"

"Enlighten me? Indeed, he has not spoken more than six words since he came to say that he is taking me to Dublin. He is not an enlivening companion, I fear. I shall have to content myself with conversing with Martha." She smiled mockingly at the captain's flushed and worried face. "Where do you think Martha can have got to?"

As though in answer to a cue, Kitty's maid came into the room, cloaked, bonneted, and vast. She quite dwarfed the slenderly built captain as she stood there, and she appeared to be seething with indignation.

"Well," she said, addressing herself to Sir William, "a fine carry-on this is, sir! The sooner we're gone the better, if you ask me. You'll never credit it, milady, but I've been held downstairs by one of those great hunks of soldiers, and when I made him let me pass, what should I find but two more of them opening your dress box that was down in the hall. I gave them a right telling-off, that I did! Opening it up and putting their dirty hands on your things."

"And did they find anything?" inquired Sir William. "They had orders to look for young Shamus Finn."

Martha folded her arms over her ample chest and said, "Oh! So it was your orders, was it? And why should he be hiding among her Ladyship's gowns, may I ask? Aren't you satisfied with treating her like dirt, turning her away . . ."

"Martha!" said Kitty firmly. "Get Robert into the carriage, do. Please!" She pushed her maid toward the bed, where Robert lay in a cocoon of blankets, sleeping profoundly. "Take him now!"

Martha went out, sniffing, and remarking that her Lady-ship needn't hurry herself for five minutes, as she still had her laundry to collect from the end of the passage. "For if you think I'm leaving here without Robert's flannel nightgowns, my name's not Martha Barley . . ."

"Collect what you please," said Kitty, "but please be ready in the carriage when I come down in ten minutes."

When Martha had gone Kitty went to the dressing table and forced herself to sit before it, peering at her reflection. "You know, William," she said in her slowest, most leisurely drawl, "I am in two minds as to whether I should wear this bonnet, or send down to the carriage for the fur-trimmed one with the high crown. What is your opinion?"

(191)

"The one you have will do, ma'am," replied Sir William with scarcely veiled impatience. "We must be gone. There is no time to change it now."

"I can tell that you do not like it," she said sadly. "I was afraid it would not do when I put it on . . ."

"It is charming," he snapped. "Now, ma'am, are you ready to leave?"

She twisted round upon the dressing-table chair to look at him. "William, it sounds as if someone has been moving all the furniture about these past few minutes—and not carefully, either. What is going on?"

"I told you," he said. "My men are looking for that boy." He glanced at Captain Dillon's tight-lipped, affronted face and added, "I am anxious for his safety, I suppose." Then, suspiciously, "You haven't by any chance seen him yourself, ma'am?"

"Of course not," she retorted. "I have been shut up here all the morning. How could I have seen him?" Her green eyes were clear and guileless, but he had seen that innocent look before and knew that it could hide all manner of things.

He looked at her for a moment longer, and then said briskly, "Come, then. I am going to ride with you to the edge of the lake, ma'am. After that I shall be obliged to go the other way."

She kept him waiting for another few minutes, and then drew on her gloves, smoothing the fingers in a careful, deliberate way, remarking that she had not yet taken leave of her host.

"Denny is otherwise engaged," said Sir William. "I will convey your thanks to him when next I see him." His pale eyes were watchful, wary. "Come!" he said once more, offering her his arm. "We must be off."

"Where is Mr. Denny?" she demanded in a low voice.

"You don't mean to say that your men are searching his house while he is away?"

"He is not away. He is merely too . . . occupied to see your Ladyship off." Sir William smiled slightly, as at some inner jest, and added, "And young Mick is unable to do so for much the same reason."

Her eyes widened, and he thought she was going to protest. However, she allowed him to lead her to the stairs. As they went down he told her that he was somewhat pressed for time, by reason of the ball which Lord Comeragh was giving at Kilnabawn that evening. Kitty managed to make show of interest in the matter, even saying that she wished she might have stayed to dance at the ball; but her whole mind was taken up with her fear for Luke's safety, and as her ears were assailed by sounds of breaking glass and splintering wood she had considerable difficulty in maintaining her calm manner.

Sir William told her that his engagement was to be announced at the ball. "You don't lose much time, do you, William?" she managed to say admiringly, and then she gave a gasp. Despite Sir William's orders that all doors leading into the hall were to be closed until Kitty had gone, one of them had been left ajar. "William!" she said after he had closed it with a resolute snap. "Did you tell your men to do that?"

"It will be set to rights," he said stiffly. "Until the boy is found, I have no choice in the matter."

She stood stock-still for several moments, fighting to remain composed. She knew that she must not stay, for Mick's sake. But how could she leave without at least knowing where Luke was? "Where is Mr. Denny, William?" she demanded. "Where is he?"

He frowned and shrugged his elegant shoulders. "If you must know, ma'am, he is temporarily in his own cellar. It is

(193)

all a tiresome political matter, and nothing which need concern you. I had not realized," he added sarcastically, "that you had developed such an interest in Denny. Mind you, he's a personable fellow, but I had not thought him to your Ladyship's taste."

"Oh, he is not at all to my taste," she agreed obligingly. "His manners are quite uncouth." She looked round the little hallway with a faraway expression in her green eyes. "But I should like to have said goodbye."

"I will give him your message."

Kitty took one last look round her, and then went quickly out of the house and into the waiting carriage. She was handed into it by Captain Dillon, and Sir William's smartly liveried groom shut the door on her. There was a lurch as the carriage began to move and a clatter of horses' hooves and a rumble of wheels upon the gravel. Kitty sank back against the leather upholstery and closed her eyes.

She did not open them at once, for she knew that to do so would be to release the hot tears. She was trembling violently and felt almost too weak to move. She clasped her gloved hands together, trying to decide what to do for the best. Plainly there was nothing she could do before Sir William left them, but she might persuade the captain to turn back after that. There was Robert's safety to be thought of, and Martha's. She wished, at this moment when so much depended on her ability to think fast, that her brain did not feel so utterly wooly.

"Martha," she said presently, still keeping her eyes closed, "I must get help to Mr. Denny. I don't know how, but you heard the noise those soldiers were making—and that is only a beginning . . ." She clasped her hands even tighter together and said, "I must help them . . . there is no one else . . ."

To Kitty's relief, Martha made no reply. She opened her

eyes and saw that her maid was bending over Robert's still soundly slumbering form, her head in its large bonnet bent forward. Kitty thought the child looked less feverish, and she wondered if she could arrange to get Martha and Robert taken to Kilkenny. She would have to enlist the captain's help. He did not look overintelligent, but there was no one else to whom she could turn.

The carriage slowed down and she peered out. Sir William came to the door, letting in a gush of cold air. He had dismounted, and stood there looking in at her. "I don't mean to stay above a minute," he said. "This must be goodbye, my dear."

Kitty held out her hand. "Indeed, I suppose so. I daresay it is for the best. Your little Miss Braxton will make you a more comfortable wife than I, I think."

"Kitty!" The words might have been wrung from him. "Kitty, how I wish it had been otherwise!"

She tried to withdraw her hand, but he would not release it. She merely said, "You had better be on your way, William."

"In a minute," he said, his blue eyes devouring her. "One more minute . . ."

"Oh, for goodness' sake, shut the door!" she said crossly. "Goodbye!"

"Kitty!" said Sir William in a tone of anguish. He lunged forward, and though Kitty shrank back against the leather squabs of the carriage, he still pressed forward and kissed her fervently on the lips.

As the door was shut and the carriage moved forward, Kitty found herself in a burning rage. She said fiercely, "Martha!" She was rubbing at her lips with her gloved hands as though trying to remove the stain of him. "Martha, if that man ever comes near me again, if he dares to call at Brook Street, you may tell Horton to throw him out."

CHAPTER SIXTEEN

KITTY JERKED ROUND as though she had been stung. It was at first quite unbelievable that Luke should be sitting there. He looked like Martha. She had never for a moment supposed that it was not Martha. But it was he! A great wave of relief and exhilaration seemed to lift her up, only to plunge her down immediately into a fear too sharp to be borne. She made a hurried movement with her hands, as though to warn him of danger.

"What in the world . . . ? What do you think you are doing? Oh, this is madness! They will see that you are gone, and they will be after us . . . ."

"No such thing. I am in my own wine cellar, and they are all busy looking for Shamus."

"What will they do when they find him?"

"They won't find him. I have taken him to Judge Moore."

"Oh!" She was so entranced to see him that she had little time to spare for wondering how Shamus had been spirited away. She said, rather shakily, "What a quiz you look in Martha's bonnet!" And then added anxiously, "And what have you done with Martha?"

"She will come to no harm. It was Martha who released me from the cellar. She saw me being led away."

He did not enlighten her as to where Martha was, however, for he was transferring Robert onto the seat beside him, saying, "There. Martha gave him a sleeping draught, so he will not wake for a while."

"Martha drugged him?" she exclaimed, trying to quell the rebellious laughter which was welling up in her at Luke's effrontery. "How ever did you persuade her to do such a shocking thing?" Then she noticed what he was doing and said sternly, "Really, sir! You cannot undress here!"

But he merely advised her to avert her eyes. "You are so delightful when you are posing as an outraged matron," he added as he struggled with Martha's bodice buttons. She watched in astonishment as he emerged from his cocoon of petticoats, and saw that he was wearing knee breeches and stockings of some dark, thin material. He looked slimmer, neater, and more intent that she had hitherto seen him, and she was reminded of their first meeting when she had thought him dangerous.

He knelt beside her on the floor of the carriage, smiling into her startled face. There was something more than amusement in his eyes. "Delightful. Why is it that whenever I see you being ridiculous I feel an urge to kiss you?"

"I am sure I cannot say, Mr. Denny," she retorted, almost overcome by his nearness and the caressing note in his voice, and determined not to show it. "You would be better to decide what is to be done next. If you don't take care, Captain Dillon will look in the carriage and see you."

He did not answer, but glanced toward the window. She watched him tensely. There were lines of tiredness about his eyes, but he was to Kitty's sight the embodiment of strength and succor, part of herself.

She reminded herself that he was in danger. She had not the least idea how to help him. She said gravely and fearfully, "What will you do now?" The carriage lurched violently and she said crossly, "I do not think much of your road."

Luke did not seem to be attending to her. He was crouching on the floor, listening intently for some expected sound from without.

"Go to the window," he ordered quietly, "and ask Dillon what is going on. Attract his attention if you can. I'll deal with the coachman and his groom."

There was no time to protest, even to think, for the carriage was already plunging to a standstill. In a moment the captain came into view. He pulled the door open, his face pinker and more serious than ever. "Don't be alarmed, ma'am," he said. "There's a crowd of tinkers on the road ahead, but we'll not be above a minute or two clearing them out of the way."

"Tinkers!" cried Kitty, leaning forward so that she was blocking the doorway of the carriage, "Oh, look at their delightful painted wagons. How charming!"

"Take care, ma'am," said the captain, steadying her. "Stay where you are, I beg of you. These persons look colorful, I grant you, but they are not overclean."

"Do you think they'll tell our fortunes, Captain Dillon?" Kitty asked in her most inane accents. "I wonder . . ."

But he had already turned from her with a furious expletive. There were more than half a dozen caravans upon the road, and on them and around them was a crowd of ragged-looking persons, ponies of all colors and sizes, dogs, and even some hobbled goats. At least a dozen scarecrows were advancing upon the carriage, milling round the plunging horses, doffing their disgraceful hats to the captain and bidding him good day in cheerful unison.

"Now, look here!" cried the captain, pink and unappreciative. "Let us pass, if you please. We are in a hurry."

"A hurry, is it?" rumbled the leading scarecrow, laying a hand on the neck of the captain's fretting horse. "Now where are you going, you and your pretty lady?" He turned to Kitty, who was gazing at him in a startled way, and above the din, called out, "Good morning to you, ma'am! Is Himself in there with you?"

The captain reined back, tried to peer past Kitty into the carriage, and this was his undoing. Too late, he realized that his pistols were being quietly whisked out of their holsters; and a moment later, swearing and protesting, he was seized by several willing pairs of arms and dragged from his steed. There was a good deal of good-humored comment and laughter as he was overpowered, and Kitty, daring at last to take her eyes from him, saw that a similar fate was being dealt out to the coachman and the once-elegant groom. Luke was seated on the coachman's box, the reins looped over his arm, waiting impassively for these convulsions to come to an end. When they had done so, he stepped down from the box and told them to bring the captain to him.

The luckless officer was propelled forward, his arms held by two burly tinkers in frieze coats. He was breathless and furious, and had become sadly muddied and disheveled in his struggles with his captors. He saw Kitty, cast her an anguished look, and said, "Have they hurt you, ma'am?" Suddenly realizing who it was standing beside her, he gasped. "Denny! You?"

"Well, George," murmured Luke, smiling. The tinkers

had grown almost silent and were watching this encounter with avid interest.

"So this is your doing?" said Captain Dillon tautly and angrily. "I really don't know what I've done to be mauled like this by your . . . friends." He spoke the final word with awful irony.

"They do appear to have been rather enthusiastic, don't they?" remarked Luke, surveying the mud upon the captain's scarlet tunic. "Well, do not worry, we'll give you a new coat, since you have dirtied that one. Joss," he said to the leader of the tinkers, "a new coat for Captain Dillon, if you please."

The captain was beginning to recover his temper, and with it his presence of mind. He retorted with a dawning grin, "You appear to be in more need of a coat than I, Denny. Why are you dressed like a damned fencing master? And for that matter, how did you get here? By God!" he exclaimed, becoming more equable with every passing second. "But I'd give a monkey to hear what Fossick has to say to this!"

There was a quick angry murmur among the tinkers at the mention of the deputy sheriff's name. Joss elbowed his way back, holding a gentleman's coat of quite passable appearance. "How will this suit your honor?" he asked, grinning cheerfully. " 'Twas lately belonging to as fine a gentleman as yourself, only he no longer wanted it . . ."

"Neither do I want it," said the captain.

"George," said Luke gently, "you have rather missed the point, I think. I need your coat myself. Give it to me, there's a good fellow, for I wouldn't like to start another brawl in front of her Ladyship."

"I'm damned if I'll part with my coat," retorted the captain, growing angry again. The hands on his arms immediately tightened their hold. He said, a shade uneasily, "What do you want with it?"

"To wear it, of course," replied Luke simply. "You shall have it back again." He turned to Kitty. "Get back into the carriage, if you please, ma'am. Robert has need of you." And when she seemed about to refuse, "Really, ma'am! You are surely not proposing to watch the poor captain being divested of his clothes. I had expected you to have more delicacy."

Kitty vanished from sight with a crisp slam of the carriage door, and he said, "Now, George?"

"Look, Denny," said the captain, "you'd be better occupied at this moment if you were to ride to Clonmel. If you got word to Colonel Forbes, he'd at least send a relief officer and some more men, so that those brutes of Fossick's might be kept within bounds. I'll write a note, if you . . ."

"There's no time, George. Your coat . . ."

"Shall I strip the clothes off of him, then?" suggested Joss, moving forward.

Luke stayed him with the shake of his head. "It's for you to decide, George. I'm wearing your uniform to Dennystown —and I want it now."

"Oh God, Denny!" said the captain, capitulating. "You're as much of a madman as your brother." He allowed himself to be led into one of the painted wagons, expostulating that Denny would never pass himself off as an officer of any kind, still less as himself.

Inside the wagon, they changed in silence. Only when Luke had forced his way into the scarlet tunic, which was much too small for comfort, did the captain say impulsively, "They'll know you for an imposter before you've taken a step inside the door."

Luke held out a hand for the captain's hat.

"What do you hope to achieve?" pursued the captain doggedly. "Listen, Denny! Duffy only takes orders from

CORPORAL MATTHEWS, guarding the door of the priest's house with two of his companions, was astonished and rather alarmed to see a troop of the high sheriff's men clattering up the road toward him. The officer at their head, who wore a fine pair of black mustaches and seemed to be in a great hurry, demanded to see the priest. He was impatient and inclined to be overbearing, and Corporal Matthews tried vainly to remonstrate with him. He did not, in fact, argue for long or with much vigor. His orders had been to let no one through, but the name of Sheriff Judkin Fitzgerald was a potent threat in the County of Tipperary. People who opposed his men did not prosper, and though Corporal Matthews had a healthy respect for Sir William Fossick, he really saw nothing for it but to let the high sheriff's officer have his way. After a brief argument, he allowed them to go by.

Father James had been considerably shaken by the morning's events, or what he knew of them, and he wondered afterward if he had appeared quite as tremulous as he felt as he fumbled to open the door to the underground passage which led from the church to Dennystown. Shaking though he was, however, he went with them, and as the little party crept along and finally climbed up the narrow stair which led to a panel at the back of Luke's tapestry hung bed, the noises from the house became increasingly alarming. It sounded as if all hell had broken loose round them. There was an unnerving smell of burning, and as they all waited tensely for Luke to unfasten the panel, there was not one of them who did not quake inwardly at what they were about to find. It seemed an age before the panel was drawn to one side, and one by one they climbed out into Luke's bedchamber. The last man was just easing himself through when the door was flung open with a crash and one of Sir William's men stood swaying on the threshold. Father James raised the clubbed stick which he held and hit the man over the head with a most satisfying and unpriestly oath.

Miss Biddy and Mary, imprisoned in the black cellar with the rest of the household, knew nothing of this. None of them ever forgot the dark airlessness of their prison and the terror of the sounds which came from above them. They had been talking among themselves, trying to keep their spirits up, but suddenly someone called for silence. There were sounds of approaching footsteps and the grating of the key in the lock. The door swung open and Luke stood there, peering in at them, the daylight from above showing that it was, miraculously, Himself who had come. Mary ran to him and clung round his neck and he picked her up in his arms and carried her up the cellar steps into the sunshine.

The smell of burning had come from the morning-room curtains, which one of the soldiers had set alight. The carnage was worst on the ground floor, where chairs had been broken, chests of drawers literally hacked to pieces. It was horribly evident that they had come to the rescue none too soon, for the blazing curtains took some time to extinguish. It was plain, too, that most of the men had not so much been looking for Shamus as using Sir William's orders as an excuse to plunder and destroy. They had helped themselves liberally to all the spirits they could find, and this made most of them easy enough to deal with.

Sergeant Duffy had been more systematic than the rest, and he was finally hunted down in the kitchen regions, where he was turning cupboards out and rooting around them with his bayonet. As his pursuers came upon him with a yell of triumph, the sergeant took one look at what seemed to be a horde of the high sheriff's men out for his blood, and took to his heels. He plunged through the kitchen window and fled into the scrub beside the lake. The tinkers tore out after him, one or two firing muskets which they had captured from the deputy sheriff's men, but they came back disconsolately after a while to report that Sergeant Duffy had escaped.

An hour or so after this, when Miss Biddy has begun to harry everyone into the business of clearing up, Judge Moore came upon Luke in the morning room.

"My God, Denny! I wish I had realized the urgency of things when you brought us the boy last night. I'd have come back with you." He looked about the morning room, which had been stripped of its charred curtains and its worst damaged furniture and wore a denuded look. "I've been in the town this morning, and they're all in an uproar over young Mick's capture. But if I'd realized what Fossick was going to do here, I'd not have wasted my time in Clonmel. I see I'm too late . . ."

"You are still very welcome," said Luke. "We're still in need of help. This matter is not finished yet, you know."

The judge eyed Luke a trifle uneasily and said, "Well, of course Fossick must be made to pay for this, but I do not think there is anything to be gained by precipitate action, my boy. You see, there are complications." He cast about in his mind as to the best way to tell Luke that anything in the nature of retaliation on his part would be the very worst thing. The judge had heard a good deal of talk in the barracks and in the other parts of the town, and had been at first indignant and incredulous at the nature of what was being said. He thought someone had been pretty busy. He knew very well how rumors could spread in a small community, and was inclined to scoff at the current tale that Mick Denny had been unmasked as the Green Man and that he and his brother up at Dennystown had been responsible for all manner of villainies and lawless acts. But he did not find it droll for long. It was unnerving to find how quickly and completely the climate of opinion could reverse itself.

People to whom the Green Man had been something of a hero only a week before were solemnly accusing him of all manner of atrocities, and it seemed a general belief that Luke, in bamboozling them all by appearing to be such a stern upholder of law and order, had somehow offended public opinion more than his scapegrace brother. It would never do for him to try to challenge Fossick at this moment, for Fossick was now the hero, with everything going in his favor. Had he not laid the Green Man by the heels, and this on the very eve of his betrothal to Miss Braxton?

He tried to tell Luke something of all this, but could not feel reassured by the grim but noncommittal expression on the other man's dark face. The judge then said something about Dennystown hardly being the same place without Paddy Joe to tell them how to go on, but from Luke's bleak expression, he regretted mentioning this subject as well. "I implore you, Denny," he said finally, "to leave this business to me. You will have justice all right; and believe me, there is going to be no hasty trial of young Mick, whatever Fossick may have implied. There are too many people who are heartily appalled at the way Kelagher was treated. Indeed, if Mick was the one who abducted him, I have to confess I admire him for it."

"He did nothing of the sort. And it is not Mick I'm concerned for, the young fool . . ."

"What then?"

Luke glanced at the judge and said evenly, "You are aware, perhaps, that Fossick almost tore this place to pieces because he wanted Shamus Finn?"

"That's what they told me out there. How fortunate that you foresaw it and brought him to me," conceded the judge, who had been some time in search of Luke and had been given several accounts of the morning's happenings before he came upon him. "But that was merely a pretext, surely?"

"No."

"But, surely?" repeated the judge, looking at Luke as though he wondered if he could know what he was saying. "What would Fossick want with the boy? Are you not letting your natural anger lead to extravagant surmises?" He gave Luke another, almost pitying glance. "A bastard child?"

In a quiet voice, which certainly held no audible trace of indignation, or of any other violent emotion, Luke told the judge the reason for his fears for Shamus. When he had finished, the judge did not speak for a short while. Then he said heavily, "If what you tell me is true, Denny, you still have no positive proof, nor would most people believe you. Don't you see, Denny," he added, when Luke darted him a look of cold hauteur, as if to indicate that other men's acceptance of his story was of small moment, "don't you see that Fossick is already a step ahead of you in this matter. If you'd heard one half of what I heard in the town this day, you'd believe it. He's doing his best to discredit you, and he's making a fine job of it."

"I'm a villain, am I?" Luke's dark eyes lit with a brief glint of laughter. "One must admire Fossick's thoroughness."

Judge Moore did not return his smile. "Frankly, Denny, if you bring out this tale now, after all this time, the whole world will merely think it an attempt to slander Fossick. Let it rest for a while, I implore you; at least until you have Mick clear of his present trouble."

"I dare not."

"But Fossick can hardly try to harm the boy after making

such a public display of wanting to get his hands on him. Denny, be reasonable!"

Luke said slowly, shaking his head, "There are too many accidents that can befall a small boy. I cannot take the risk, Judge. Nor can Fossick afford to fail. This matter has gone beyond recall."

"You'll never get anyone to believe you. More than likely, no one will agree to listen to you in the first place."

"In that case," said Luke, shrugging, "I shall demand a hearing." He turned as the tinker Joss came rather precipitately into the room. "What now?" he demanded. "I told you to take Lady Kitty to Kilkenny . . ."

"Denny!" cried Joss, without even acknowledging the judge's presence. "Denny! The lady and the captain have run out on me. They've taken the carriage and are away down the glen without anyone seeing where they went after that."

WHEN LUKE and the tinker band had clattered away down the road to Dennystown, Kitty had been convulsed by a spasm of almost hysterical laughter. It was some time before she recovered, and by the time she did so, both she and the captain were being borne off by the remaining tinkers (mainly women, children, and a few old men), and found themselves every bit as much their prisoners as Sir William's coachman and groom.

When they arrived at an encampment, a well-concealed quarry at the side of the road, a tinker girl appeared rather shyly at the carriage door. She offered to take Robert and Kitty into her caravan, and it was while the two women were bending over the child's still sleeping form that Kitty asked the girl to help her to escape. If she could only get to Clonmel, she said, help could be brought to beleaguered Dennystown.

With the help of this girl, Kitty, Captain Dillon, and Robert managed to slip away from the camp. As was to be expected, Robert woke before they were halfway to the town, and by the time they arived at Captain Dillon's lodgings, Kitty was once more only too glad to relinquish him, this time into the kindly, doting care of the captain's housekeeper.

They were disappointed when they reached the barracks, however, for the colonel was away and none of the other officers could be persuaded to go to Luke's aid that day. One of them agreed to lend them a driver for their carriage, but the travelers were weary in limb and in spirit by the time they set off for the jail with the intention of seeing Mick—even though they had little hope of doing so.

They were luckier than they had dared to hope. The captain came to Kitty, who was still sitting in the carriage, and said, "Come, ma'am, you may see him. Fossick has forbidden it, but I had a word with one of the men."

He led her past some wooden-faced soldiers into an evil-smelling cell. She saw that Mick was chained to the wall. He seemed dazed and did not at once recognize her. Then he gulped, tried to rise, but was hampered by the weight of chains upon his legs and arms. He fell back. "L . . . Lady Kitty!"

"Stay still, Mick. Why have they chained you up so? Do they think you're a dog?"

He gazed at her, his eyes holding a mixture of hope and doubt. "I never expected to see you here. Fossick said . . ." He noticed Captain Dillon standing behind her, and said, "Oh, so you've come back, too, have you, George? Are you going to get them to take off these damned uncomfortable irons?"

"I dare not, Mick. Fossick expressly ordered me to leave them on."

"Oh, Fossick! So I've him to thank for them, have I?" said the prisoner in a rather unconvincing attempt at sounding unconcerned. "I've already been honored by a visit from him. Mighty smug he was, and full of your crazy notion that I'm the Green Man. He wouldn't believe that it was all part of the jest . . ."

"Don't you see," put in Kitty, "William wishes to believe that you are the Green Man. It was he who got Cullen to bring you here—at least that is what Mr. Denny believes."

"Impossible!"

"It is quite true, Mick."

He nodded slowly, still wearing a look of strained puzzlement, as though he had difficulty in groping for the meaning of what she said. He had, in truth, been near to despair before his visitors came in. At first he had pinned his hopes upon Luke coming to his rescue, but as the hours had passed and still Luke did not come, he began to feel himself abandoned. It had been while he was in this low state of mind that Sir William Fossick had been to see him; and if he had been despondent before the deputy sheriff's visit, he was in a parlous condition after it. There would be no help for him, Sir William assured him. His brother was as deep in trouble as he was himself, and he need not think to look for aid from Kitty or Captain Dillon; they were on their way to Dublin and were no longer interested in him. Bewildering though it was to see them both now in his cell, it was a great relief.

Kitty knelt down upon the straw. "We may not stay long, but tell me, Mick, have you been well treated?"

He did not tell of what they had done to Lenehan, or of what the deputy sheriff had threatened if he did not tell him

(211)

of Kelagher's whereabouts. Nor did he tell her how very much afraid he was becoming. He had not at all liked the gloating look in Sir William's pale eyes. He said with a passable degree of nonchalance, "Oh, they gave me something to eat, all right. It's just these confounded chains that get in my way all the time. But tell me, ma'am, is it true that Fossick has locked Luke up?"

Kitty hesitated, uncertain whether she should tell him of her hopes and fears for Luke. The young man had enough to bear on his own account; there seemed little point in worrying him with further uncertainties. She said as airily as she could, "Oh, you need not worry your head about Mr. Denny. When I last saw him he was in full control of the situation."

"But Fossick said . . ."

"You need not think that William Fossick has the last word on every subject," said Kitty severely. "He has certainly not heard the last of me, at all events. All you have to do, Mick, is to keep up your spirits until you hear from me. All will be well, I promise you. And you may be sure that I shall not neglect to give William a scold for his treatment of you."

"How I should like to see you do so," he exclaimed with a shadow of a grin.

As Captain Dillon handed Kitty back into the carriage again and took his seat beside her, he asked curiously what plan she had in mind. Did she really think that the deputy sheriff would be daunted, or deflected from his aims, by a trimming from her?

"Of course I do not, but I had to say something. That poor boy was terrified out of his wits."

"All very well, ma'am, but having given him some hope, how do you propose to fulfill it?" he looked at her in exasperation. "You do not, surely, mean to speak to Fossick? If there had been anything to say to him, you might have said it this morning."

"And so might you, Captain Dillon," she retorted distantly. "I did not notice that you made any objection to the way William was going on . . ."

"That's unfair!" he cried angrily. "I am a soldier, and while it is my misfortune to be loaned to Fossick for this business, I must obey him. I have wished, I don't know how many times, that I'd never been posted to this wretched country!"

Neither of them spoke for a while. They were once more on the move, on the way to Hearn's Hotel, where the captain had bespoken a room for Kitty. Kitty gazed glumly out of the carriage window. Suddenly she gave a gasp. Tumbling to her knees, trying to see better, she cried, "Stop! Stop!"

The captain said in a weary voice, "What's the matter now, ma'am?"

"Pull the check string," she implored him, still straining to see out of the window. She was too late. The carriage moved on inexorably, and the large, menacing figure which she had so briefly glimpsed had gone from sight. "It was that sergeant William brought with him! I could swear it! What can he have been skulking there for?"

"Duffy?" he said sharply.

She nodded.

"Nonsense," said the captain irritably. "You must have been mistaken. It is quite dark, after all. Duffy was left in charge at Dennystown . . ."

"It was he, Captain Dillion!" Kitty insisted.

"Impossible."

"Turn back," she implored him. "Only turn back, and we may be sure!"

(213)

But the captain would not. If she wished to change her dress and make herself presentable enough to cajole the deputy sheriff into a more obliging frame of mind, he reminded her sourly, she had better lose no more time.

WHILE KITTY WAS DRESSING, the captain went back to the jail with the intention of speaking to the governor. He thought he might agree to make Mick more comfortable. He found the place in an uproar, and the prison doctor pushed past him as he went in. The passage leading to Mick's cell was thronged with exclaiming people who drew aside to let the doctor though. Captain Dillon was about to follow him when the prison governor came out.

He was looking pained. "I wish you military fellows would keep your prisoners in the barracks where they belong. That Denny boy has tried to do away with himself. How he got hold of a pistol, I don't know."

"He . . . he's been shot?"

"Through the chest."

"Tell me!"

"This I will tell you," returned the governor, struggling to find words to voice his resentment. "I'm not having Fossick laying the blame for this on any of my men. He's just been found, lying there in his blood, and none of those dolts of yours seem to have the least notion how he managed it."

The captain thought he knew very well how it had been done, and with bitter clarity he saw that it had been in his power to prevent it. "Duffy," he said in an agonized voice. "It must have been Duffy . . ."

The governor looked at him in an inimical way and asked him to make his meaning clearer.

The captain turned to one of his stunned-looking men.

"Has Sergeant Duffy been here? You know, Sir William Fossick's man."

"Aye, sir. He was in the building some minutes back. Honest to God, Captain, if we'd thought the lad would be trying to shoot himself, we'd not have left him for an instant."

"Duffy shot him," retorted Captain Dillon in a bitter, even tone. "If Mick dies, I'll do all in my power to see Duffy hang."

CHAPTER SEVENTEEN

CULLEN HAD SPENT the greater part of the day among the ruins of what had once been the Finns' farm. He had slept for a while among those desolate, fire-blackened walls, but after a time sleep had deserted him. It was by no means the first time Cullen had found himself alone and outcast, forced to lie up until it was once again safe to venture out, but the sense of isolation was more bitter than he had ever known it. Even though he was not being hunted, it had been natural to his cautious nature to wait until dusk before going to Mount Comeragh Lodge to claim his reward.

The day stretched on and on. He thought that he must be getting soft that he should be so haunted by the spine-chilling conviction that there were eyes all around him, watching him, condemning him, hemming him in. To keep his tormented mind on other things, Cullen fidgeted about among the ruined walls, picking up a charred piece of furniture here, discovering an earthenware cooking pot intact and wishing that he dared to kindle a fire. He did not dare.

Feeling thirsty, he looked for the old well, and while reaching down into it to scoop up some water, he came across the little iron-banded chest. It was pushed in upon a ledge, only a foot or two from the water, and the sight of it made him forget both his forebodings and his thirst.

It was not a very large chest, barely eight inches in either direction, and Cullen remembered vividly how he had once seen Katie Finn with it. She had been standing near the window of the farmhouse kitchen, and when he had rapped upon the pane, she had closed down the lid. He had asked her what she kept in it, but she had merely smiled in that distant, dreaming way of hers and had put the little coffer back upon the kitchen dresser.

Pulling the chest from the well, Cullen forced it open. At first he thought that there was nothing in it but mildewed papers and letters, and what looked like accounts in a bundle. It was only when he pulled these out, rather disgusted that there was not even a guinea or two there, that he came across the locket. It was a pretty thing, the sort of trinket that lovers give each other, with a knot of hair beneath a small circle of glass.

Cullen wondered which of Katie's admirers had given her this trinket. It must have been one of the wealthier ones, for unless his eyes deceived him, real diamonds encircled the glass. He bundled the papers back into the chest and replaced it in the well. The locket he put in his pocket. It rightly belonged, he thought, to young Shamus Finn; and it pleased him to think that he might give it to the boy before he left for the new world—for he had made up his mind to leave Ireland once he had claimed his reward from the deputy sheriff.

He came into Sir William's book-room by the long window, treading so softly that the deputy sheriff had the impression he had suddenly materialized at his elbow. "Oh, it's you," he said ungraciously. "I've another task for you."

"And what is it you're wanting this time, sir?" Cullen did not sound enthusiastic.

Sir William was in his evening clothes, an elegant figure. He waved Cullen to a seat and said, "I wonder . . ." He had the air of one who hesitates on the brink of a decision. Then he said in a peremptory tone, "You did not stay to be congratulated after you had delivered young Denny into our hands."

Cullen muttered, "I didn't want congratulations, your honor."

"No, you wanted—and you still want—your money, don't you, eh?" Sir William smiled broadly. "You may come and collect it tomorrow, Cullen. Tonight I really have no time to attend to it."

Cullen said sharply, "I must have it now, sir."

Sir William did not care for the man's tone. He had certainly been useful, but he needed to be taught a lesson. "You will be paid in due course," he said dismissively.

But Cullen remained seated. "I want the money now, sir. I gave Mick Denny into your hands, God forgive me."

"Oh, come," said Sir William lightly and contemptuously, "don't pretend that you're suffering from remorse, man. I know it's only the gold you care for, and for that you'll have to wait. I am already overdue at Kilnabawn." He pulled open one of the drawers of his writing table and handed Cullen a small leather bag. "Here. There's twenty guineas on account. It's all I can give you this evening."

He was somewhat relieved when Cullen reached for the

bag and began to count the contents. It would not do to antagonize Cullen at this moment. He knew too much; and besides, he wished to use him further. He watched the man testing each of the gold coins carefully between his yellowed teeth before he put them back in the bag, and when he had finished, he said, "Why are you in such a hurry for the money? Are your debts so pressing?"

"I'm leaving the country, sir."

"You are prudent. This double game you play must have its drawbacks. Where do you mean to go?"

"To America, sir."

Sir William's pale blue eyes rested on Cullen consider-ingly, bright and sharp with interest. "Indeed? Well, you should be safe enough from Denny's avenging arm there. This is the second time you've incurred his wrath, is it not?" He chuckled and said, "You are wise to take your gold and run for it. Perhaps if you were to assist me in one small matter, I could manage to give you the money tonight . . ."

Cullen's eyes lifted momentarily to Sir William's. "I'd be mighty obliged if you would, your honor. There's a ship that sails from Waterford tomorrow . . ."

"Ah," murmured the deputy sheriff. "And you hope to sail on it?" For a few moments he appeared to be lost in thought, and Cullen, eying him surreptitiously, did not feel that he was going to get his money easily. "Tell me," said Sir William softly, "did anyone see you coming here this eve-ning?"

Cullen shook his head. He did not deem it necessary to tell the deputy sheriff that he had, in fact, been seen by Miss Fossick. That lady had been in front of an upstairs window, gazing out into the garden. She had been in a state of un-dress, and from the scandalized haste with which she had withdrawn from his sight, it seemed unlikely that she would mention their brief exchange of glances.

Sir William was asking him when he meant to join the ship, and from where and when it was supposed to sail. When the deputy sheriff had possessed himself of these details, he began to hum a little tune under his breath. Cullen did not like it. It was well known that Sir William was never so dangerous as when he was jovial, and he wondered what was coming next.

He had not long to wait. Quietly Sir William said, "Did you know that Katie Finn's child is living at Dennystown?"

Cullen was startled into looking straight at Sir William. The deputy sheriff was still smiling.

"Well?" said Sir William incisively. "Did you know of it?"

"I did that, sir," returned Cullen, still gazing at the deputy sheriff as though he hoped to learn more by studying his handsome face.

"And have you a notion to earn another five hundred guineas?"

Cullen nodded.

"That will be in addition to the thousand pounds I promised you, of course," pursued Sir William smoothly, marking with satisfaction the growing gleam of enthusiasm in the other man's eyes.

Cullen's eyes dropped to the leather top of the writing table. "And what is it I'm to do, sir?"

"Find this boy," Sir William said in his decided fashion, "and take him with you on that ship. I shall come out to the vessel before noon tomorrow, and if you have carried out my instructions, I shall pay you all that I have promised." Cullen was still sitting with his eyes downcast, and his uncommunicative face caused Sir William to say rather testily, "Well? I should have thought this money would be just what you need to give you a start in the new world. Aren't you capable of grasping that fact?"

Cullen was, indeed, trying without success to grasp at

some reason for Sir William's extraordinary request. What did he mean by the boy? Why did he want him removed from the country? Was he, perhaps, the child's father? It was well enough known that Sir William had taken a fancy to Katie Finn, but in this he was only one of many. Cullen found it strange—and unnerving—and was in the unusual position of wishing he might cast the deputy sheriff's bribe back in his smiling face. He had a fondness for Shamus, the small red-headed urchin whom he had met from time to time playing truant from his lessons. Cullen, having perhaps a natural sympathy with anyone who was on the run from authority, had more than once aided and abetted him, and had even taken him fishing on one occasion. He wished it had been anyone but Shamus.

Sir William was still waiting for his answer. "Well, man, are you struck dumb?"

"What if I hadn't the notion to take the boy with me, sir?"

"Then you'll sail without your money—any of it." Sir William's flatly spoken retort only partially veiled his impatience. "Come, man, I'm not asking much of you. I shall make no inquiries into what you do with the boy after you sail; and if you obey my instructions, no one will know where he is gone. If he should succumb to a fever, or be swept overboard, no one will be any the wiser." Sir William laughed softly. "But perhaps you are in too great a dread of Denny . . ."

"I'll do it, sir," said Cullen quietly, his brain seething with surmises. Could it be that Sir William was ridding himself of his by-blow, now that respectability had become a matter of first·importance to him? If Sir William was willing to pay such a large sum to get the child away, there might be those who would bid higher for him to stay. Denny, for instance? His thoughts shied away from that. Still, there might be some way to turn this unaccountable situation to his advantage. He raised his head. "How do I know that I'll get paid? You could always miss the tide, and I've paid for my passage already. Give me the money tonight, your honor, and I'll do it!"

"You'll have it when you and the boy are where I want you to be," retorted Sir William, shrugging his elegant shoulders. The spy cast him a malevolent look, and he added disdainfully, "Do not judge all men by your own rather peculiar standards. You will get your money. Believe me, I'll be glad to see you both gone."

It seemed that Cullen was convinced at last.

AS HE CLIMBED the last steep hill to the Finns' farm, Cullen's thoughts were still scurrying this way and that. He was no nearer to any conclusions, but he was conscious of a growing reluctance to take Shamus with him. It suddenly came to him that Katie Finn's little chest might hold a clue to Shamus's parentage, or provide him with some light on the mystery, so he groped his way across the courtyard and found the gap where the main door used to be. He pulled an end of candle from his coat pocket and devised a kind of candlestick by wedging it between two stones. When the small flame had struggled into precarious life, he hurried to the place where the chest was hidden. He knelt upon the stone slabs of the floor, and with fingers that were clumsy with haste and excitement he opened the lid. He expected to see the bundle of documents, but there was nothing of the kind in the little chest. Incredulously, he bent closer, putting his hand into the bottom of it to touch what lay within. It felt damp and leafy to his fingers, and when he took it out and held it to the light, he saw that it was a piece of ivy.

A small sound at his back sounded to Cullen like a thunderclap of doom. Slowly he turned. The ivy leaves were still in his hand. A tall cloaked figure was standing only a few yards away, unmoving, yet infinitely menacing. The whole of this apparition's face was covered by a mask. Only the slits of the eyes seemed alive; and very much alive they seemed. It was too dark to see the color of the man's cloak, but Cullen did not need to see it.

"Oh!" he exclaimed weakly. "You'll be the one they call the Green Man, I'm thinking. And here was I telling them that it was Mister Mick Denny. You should be grateful to me for that, sir."

"Should I?" replied the Green Man softly in a voice which chilled Matthew Cullen to the very soul. "Should I indeed? I wonder why you should think so. But you shall tell me presently. For the moment, tell me what you are doing with Katie Finn's box!"

CHAPTER EIGHTEEN

KITTY AND CAPTAIN DILLON were told, when they called at Mount Comeragh Lodge, that the deputy sheriff and his sister had already left for the ball at Kilnabawn. This was a setback, but Kitty was in no mood to allow Sir William to evade her, and a couple of hours later she and Captain Dillon found themselves bowling up Lord Comeragh's tree-lined avenue.

The captain was in an even greater state of gloom and trepidation than ever, but he still felt obliged to go with his infuriating charge. As they neared the end of the avenue he said without much hope, "We can still turn back. You know very well that it would be the only prudent thing to do, ma'am."

"Oh, I know it," she retorted sweetly, "for you have said so a hundred times. And as I have told you as often, Captain Dillon, there was really no need for you to come. You did not sound so doubtful when you first told me that Mick had been shot. Do you wish to confront William with this crime, or do you not?"

"Of course I do," the captain protested in a voice which was almost a groan. "But not at Lord Comeragh's ball! I might remind your Ladyship, for one thing, that you were not even invited . . ."

"No, indeed!" she agreed with a gurgle of laughter. "Do try to summon up your sense of the ridiculous, Captain Dillon. Doesn't it cheer you, even a little, to think that I shall be attending William's betrothal party while he has been solemnly assuring his future mama-in-law that I am safely on my way to Dublin? How fortunate that it is a masked ball! We should never have managed otherwise."

Captain Dillon did not smile. He watched her shadowy, masked profile, saw the diamonds glinting in her ears and the infinitely graceful carriage of her head, and was by no means entranced. He acknowledged that she was lovely, but her beauty did not stir him, unless it was to dislike. She was heartless, uncaring. It was all very well for her to take it all so blithely, making a mock of it all. In a dim way he felt that she was to blame for the whole business, and it made it worse that she was the only one who had no real stake in it.

She would come out of it all unscathed, this sharp-tongued society darling. The grim realities of it would not touch her at all; and whatever might happen to the rest of them (Dennystown laid waste, Denny ruined, Mick imprisoned or hanged, or, as seemed possible, dying of his wound, himself court-martialed for disobeying orders), Kitty would go back to the world she knew, essentially unhurt and unperturbed. She might, for a while, express her sense of shock at the violence and disorderliness of the Irish, and she would be richer by a few droll anecdotes about the Irish scene with which to regale her acquaintances, but none of it would really affect her.

He did her an injustice. Kitty was not unconcerned. She was in the grip of a consuming disgust and anger at what had been done to Mick in prison. She could think of nothing else —of nothing but the moment when she would confront William Fossick with his henchman's crime. She found it easy enough to share the captain's conviction that Sir William had ordered it; she now thought him capable of anything. Somehow, Kitty was determined that he must be confronted with his villainy, publicly accused of it, and if no one else came forward to do it, she would accuse him herself. She had been too late to prevent the dastardly shooting of Mick in his cell, but if William Fossick could be shamed, browbeaten, or prevailed upon to take his men from Dennystown and leave Luke Denny and his people in peace, that alone would have been worth doing.

They swept up to Kilnabawn, and through the open door they saw the hall aglow with the light of many candles. Evidently Lord Comeragh, unaccustomed and averse as he was to entertaining his neighbors, had decided to do so in style.

"Do smile, Captain Dillon," urged Kitty as he handed her out of the carriage. "If you look so glum and apprehensive you will be under suspicion before you have stepped inside the door. They will positively know us for interlopers."

"Since Lord Comeragh invited me personally, ma'am, I hardly think that will happen to me."

"Well, then, strive to look a little more cheerful," she adjured him as they went into the huge pillared hall. Bowing flunkeys ushered them in, and they mounted the flight of stairs which led to the long gallery. The butler hurried to greet them and told the captain, whom he recognized, that the guests were dancing in the red drawing room. Kitty was led upstairs to take off her cloak, and she was handing it to a maid and peering at her masked reflection in a long mirror, when a lady hurried into the room.

She was not a young lady, though she had the fluttering diffident voice of a shy schoolgirl. She addressed the maid tentatively, as though she was fearful of doing so, and begged her in an apologetic way to find her some small box in which to put her broken string of pearls. "I do not know how I came to break it . . . Indeed, I don't."

"Never mind, Miss Fossick," said the maid soothingly, "I'll fetch you something to put them in. Just you go down again to the dancing, and I'll leave your pearls in the dressing-table drawer."

Kitty had made no plan as to what she would do, once at the ball, but that William's sister should be there beside her seemed too good an opportunity to miss. When the maid had gone, she stepped up to Miss Fossick and addressed her quietly by name.

Miss Fossick jumped nervously, and said with a little gasp that she hadn't seen anyone there.

"No?" murmured Kitty softly. "Then you must allow me to present myself. I am Kitty Harcombe, ma'am, and I am charmed that we are permitted to meet after all."

If Miss Fossick had looked nervous before, she looked positively hunted at this, and stood in front of Kitty, clenching her trembling hands on the strings of her discarded mask and shaking her faded fair head in a disbelieving way. "Oh, no!" she breathed in a horrified voice. "No!"

"Oh, but it is true, you know," drawled Kitty, her lips smiling below her black velvet mask. "You did not expect me, I see, and I do not somehow think that your delightful brother will expect to see me here, either," Miss Fossick seemed to quail. "Will he ask me to stand up with him, do you

(227)

think?" Kitty inquired sweetly. "For old times' sake. Do you think he will? He dances so gracefully."

Miss Fossick looked as if she was finding it difficult to breathe. She groped her way to a chair and collapsed on it.

"Are you surprised?" inquired the hateful drawling voice above her head. "I cannot understand why you should, ma'am, for it was your compelling letters which gave me such a notion to come into Ireland . . ."

"Lady Kitty," Miss Fossick managed to say weakly, "it is very . . . wrong of you to come. You will spoil all . . ."

Kitty had turned and was studying herself in a long mirror. Behind her own reflection she could see Miss Fossick crouching, cowering in her chair. "Spoil all?" she repeated coolly. "No, I shall not. On the contrary, I mean to provide just that extra entertainment, ma'am, which will make the evening memorable."

Miss Fossick clasped her hands together as though she were praying, which in a way she was. Her head was swimming again and she had forgotten to bring her powders with her. She said in a monotone, "Lady Kitty, you must go away."

"Go away and miss dear William's betrothal party?" Kitty said in an astonished tone. "Why so, indeed?" Her voice hardened and lost some of its laughing lilt. "Miss Braxton is rather a young lady for William to take to wife, is she not? It would be fairer, don't you think, if she were told the truth about the man she is about to wed?"

Miss Fossick was muttering to herself and rocking to and fro as though she were in pain, though she never once took her agonized gaze away from Kitty's face. "Why did you come here?" she said in a shaking whisper. "He'll never marry you! Never!"

"How fortunate for me," said Kitty in a steely voice. "I have no wish to wed a murderer!"

Miss Fossick's somewhat protruding eyes looked about

ready to start out of her head. "Murderer?" she echoed. "Oh, no! It is not true . . ."

"Oh, yes, ma'am," Kitty went on implacably. "You cannot hide from it forever, you know. Your brother is a murderer. There is blood on his hands, innocent blood . . ."

"No! No!" Miss Fossick cried out shrilly. "It was not true. He told me it was not true. It was a nightmare . . ."

Kitty stared at the terror-stricken woman in astonishment. Persecuting her was like tormenting a wounded animal, and yet if she knew of Sir William's responsibility for Mick's attempted murder, Kitty intended that she would admit it. Fiercely she pursued her point. "You knew! He wanted him dead, didn't he?"

Miss Fossick's eyes, clinging to Kitty's, seemed to look beyond her to a vision of horror. She said in a tired, hopeless tone, "I get so muddled with it all. It is so long since I have dared to sleep, for fear that the nightmare will come again." Pathetically, she went on, "He told me to forget it, but I cannot do so. Sometimes, when I have taken too many of my powders, I cannot be sure whether I am awake or dreaming."

Kitty said more mildly, "I have no wish to distress you, ma'am, but if you know that Sir William ordered Mick's murder, you must in justice be prepared to say so."

Miss Fossick jerked upright, echoing Mick's name in a startled tone.

"Oh, don't try to pretend now," said Kitty contemptuously. "To have a man shot while he was chained to the wall is surely more than even you can condone."

But Miss Fossick seemed determined to deny it. In a remarkably revived tone she assured Kitty that Sir William had been entirely innocent of Mick's wounding. Why, he had been miles away when the news was brought and had been shocked beyond measure.

"Oh, I don't doubt it," returned Kitty sarcastically. In

spite of disappointment she could not help wondering at Miss Fossick's sudden recovery. A moment earlier she had been positively overcome, and within seconds of hearing Mick's name she had changed, had become almost animated in her stuttering efforts to say that Sir William had been utterly innocent. If Miss Fossick thought her brother innocent of that, thought Kitty fleetingly, of what had she thought him guilty? What nightmare of horror had he ordered her to forget? She set this query aside, however, and said, "I suppose that Sir William would force you to vouch for him, so I shall not blame you. Let us go down to the ball. Who knows? I may get an opportunity to ask him about it myself."

Miss Fossick gripped hold of Kitty's long velvet sleeve as though to detain her by force. "You cannot . . . Oh, pray do not try to mar William's happiness, Lady Kitty! If only you would go away now and come and see him in the morning. The judge is to announce the betrothal at midnight, you must know, and it would be a shocking thing if anything were to spoil it."

"At midnight?" echoed Kitty in a startled voice. She had not known there was so little time. A clock on the mantel shelf showed that it wanted only ten minutes to twelve. "Stay here if you wish, ma'am," she said curtly, pulling her sleeve ungently from Miss Fossick's clammy grasp and starting on her way. "But I must go."

Miss Fossick stood still, incapable of movement. She did not know what to do for the best. Should she warn William? To do so would, in all probability, only bring his wrath down upon her, and he would, she knew, be amazingly angry. She took a faltering step toward the door. If only her head would cease from swimming so! If only she could decide what best to do!

Then matters were taken out of her hands. As she reached the foot of the stairs Mrs. Moore pounced upon her and begged her to bear her company for a few minutes. Miss Fossick saw Kitty disappearing down the long, flower-decked gallery and knew that she had lost her chance to do anything about it.

AFTER THE SECOND COUNTRY DANCE Judge Moore found his way to the low, flower-banked dais where Lord Comeragh had been holding court. He sank down into a chair beside the earl. His Lordship, a vast figure with an empurpled, bloated face and a gouty foot swathed in bandages, was in excellent humor. He sat there staring happily at the dancing masked throng (his own face was bare, of course), and his little sandy-lashed eyes were shrewd and full of life. "Ah, Moore," he said to the perspiring judge. "Dancing's hard work, eh?"

The judge said with a grunt, "What made you decide that we were to wear these damned uncomfortable nose-bags, Comeragh?" He removed his own mask as he spoke and mopped his damp countenance with a large silk handkerchief. "Don't you like our faces? You'll have to suffer mine, at all events, for I need to cool off."

" 'Twas some fool notion of Amelia's, I fancy," growled his Lordship. "She actually opened her mouth and said she'd like a masked ball, and all of us were so astonished to hear the chit express an opinion that we nearly fell over backwards," With a wheezing guffaw, the earl leaned toward the judge and added, "If that gel of Euphemia's has two original thoughts to rub together, I've yet to see a sign of them. Still, women with ideas are always the ones to give trouble, and William will do well enough with Amelia. With what I'll settle on them, and my name behind them, young William should go far. You've heard that William's laid the Green Man by the heels?"

"Aye, I hear so," returned the judge unemotionally. He

scanned the crowd of masked and gaily clad persons, and was easily able to distinguish Sir William's tall, elegant form. Even as the judge watched him, Sir William flung back his fair head and laughed at something which was being said. He was in high fettle. "Aye," repeated the judge, "he told me of it himself."

"Only let the rascal tell us where Kelagher is hid," said the earl fiercely, "and we'll string them both up and see an end to them. It can't be too soon for my liking."

"Young Denny may not come to trial at all, you know," said the judge grimly, and he told the earl what he had learned from the prison doctor. The earl, however, far from expressing sorrow at this shocking news, was only alarmed lest the Green Man should die without disclosing Kelagher's whereabouts.

" 'Tis a damned disgrace, Moore. The feller should never've had the means to do away with himself. It's nothing short of negligence, and so I told William . . ."

"Fossick was mighty put out about it, I hear."

"He'll be more than put out if Kelagher isn't found," said Lord Comeragh with an angry snort. "They'll have to make young Denny tell them . . ."

"He'll be in no state to be questioned for some time." The judge paused, and added, "Indeed, if he pulls through . . ."

"Ha! Just give me five minutes alone with the villain!" retorted his Lordship, grasping his gold-handled walking stick in a vindictive fashion, "and he'd tell me . . . Stands to reason he knows where Kelagher is, for he'd never have tried to take his own life if he'd not been guilty. A cowardly, unbalanced thing to do. But it's no more than I would expect from that stable, Moore—that yellow streak, yer know. Look at old Mick Denny! Drank himself to death."

The judge did not attempt to argue. He merely said mildly, "Well, you know, Comeragh, this Green Man's progress would seem to me to be the work of a careful, methodical mind. I can't for the life of me see Mick Denny as the brains of it—not of the Kelagher affair. It was too smooth and co-ordinated."

The earl pursed his swollen lips and shot the judge a sly, triumphant glance. "William thinks it's Luke Denny who's behind the whole thing. He believes him to be the prime mover in it, and he's got him penned up in Dennystown for the moment, out of harm's way."

"Luke Denny? Impossible!" retorted the judge emphatically. "He's no more the Green Man than I am."

"William's sure of it."

"Then he'll have to prove it," returned Judge Moore tartly.

The judge had already met with several versions of this theory, and the idea that Luke, not Mick, was the organizer and instigator of all the Green Man's activities had become an accepted thing. Some said that Mick would never last the night (and really, one person said, it would be for the best if he died—no one wanted a horrid scandal of a trial).

All through the evening the judge's sense of unease had been growing. He knew very well how strong could be the force of public opinion. In times of stress, a mere breath of a rumor could become a gale force of popular conviction by the mere frequency of its telling. He did not like it. Under the laughter and the gala atmosphere of the ball, he sensed a witch-hunting spirit. If Mick Denny died, a scapegoat would have to be found. It looked as if Luke had already been cast in this rôle; and knowing, as he did, something of Luke's intentions for the evening, he felt very uneasy indeed.

He had tried to remonstrate with Sir William, "Now, Fossick," he had said, rather sternly, "you've heard what they're saying. You know very well that Denny was wholly against

Mick's United notions and would never countenance his brother flouting the law."

"That's what Denny would have us believe, at all events," returned Sir William with smiling lips. His eyes stayed hidden behind the obligatory mask. "If Denny is innocent, as you seem to think, let him prove himself so." And with these words, Sir William turned away.

From his seat beside Lord Comeragh, the judge could see that the hands of the clock pointed to five minutes to twelve. He scanned the masked, shifting, chattering figures of the guests, and tried in vain to discern which one was Luke. The judge would have given a great deal to have warned him how things stood.

He saw a woman cross the floor to where the deputy sheriff was holding court. He had only seen Kitty Harcombe once at Dennystown, but the regal carriage of her head and the shining pale hair were unmistakable. His sense of misgiving grew. He watched his wife come in with Miss Fossick, and together they sat down upon a small sofa near the dais.

Sir William had turned aside for a moment to murmur an instruction in the ear of a passing flunkey, and turned round to find his path blocked by a lady in a black velvet mask. She wore a black velvet gown with long trailing sleeves, and had an almost medieval appearance.

"Good evening, William," she said sweetly.

At the sound of Kitty's voice, Sir William felt as if a pit had opened at his feet. He gazed down at her incredulously.

"This is a moment of triumph for you, isn't it, William?" she went on in her gentle, drawling voice. "The Green Man taken, and all the highest and most illustrious of your neighbors thronged here to hear of your betrothal? It would be a pity to mar it, would it not?"

"I must ask you to leave, ma'am," said Sir William in a low, vehement tone. "This is no time for vulgar jests."

"Pray, be careful!" she said softly and sharply, raising her right arm. She was standing with her back to the main part of the ballroom, so that only Sir William could see the muzzle of the small pistol which protruded from the folds of her sleeve. "You see," she went on chidingly, "you must not be hasty, nor try to hustle me out of the way. Such an ungentlemanly way to go on, William! Do you not mean me to stay and drink to your health?"

"For pity's sake, ma'am," he said eying the pistol uneasily. "Don't make a scene, for pity's sake!"

"For pity's sake," she repeated slowly. She smiled a little, crookedly, and then said simply, "But whoever suggested that I should do anything so ill-bred as to make a scene? Come"—she gave him quite a hard prod with the muzzle of the pistol, and added—"Come. You shall sit beside me and tell me who they all are."

He had no choice but to go where she urged him, and they moved side by side to a brocaded chair beside the dais. Kitty disposed herself upon it gracefully and suggested that Sir William should sit at her side. "This is delightful," she remarked amiably. "Of course, I know Lady Braxton by sight. What bravery, William, to be taking such a dragon for a mama-in-law! For my part, I'd sooner face the gallows."

"Kitty . . ."

"Now who is the gentleman by her Ladyship's side? The stout one with his foot bandaged? Do sit down, William, and then I shall not be obliged to speak so loudly." Her enticing pink lips curved again into a smile as he plumped himself down on the other brocaded chair. She said coolly, "And there is Judge Moore. I recognize him all right. Is this the moment to unmask, I wonder?"

"Kitty, this has gone far enough!" he whispered imploringly. He reached for her left hand, which had strayed to the fastening of her black velvet mask. "Indeed, it has gone too far!"

She allowed him to take her hand, and said coolly, "Why, yes. It certainly has gone too far. You went too far, William, when you tricked Mick Denny into playing the Green Man." She saw him swallow convulsively. "And I hear," she added relentlessly, "that he may be dead before morning."

"That was by his own hand," he said quickly. His usually cool brain was refusing to serve him properly. He was expected up on the dias, and he saw Lady Braxton making urgent signs to him. But Kitty's pistol was still pressed against his ribs, and if he tried to rise, the chances were that she would rise with him. He was penned, helpless, unable to move a muscle for fear of what she might do.

Judge Moore decided that he could not put off the moment any longer. He rose to his feet, and amid general merriment invited everyone to remove their masks. There were some ironic cheers, and mask strings were undone with alacrity. There followed cries of astonishment and a few ladylike shrieks. Everyone was so busy, in fact, that it was some time before anyone noticed a number of cloaked and hooded figures that had appeared at each one of the several doors and windows of the ballroom.

The judge saw them, of course, because he had been expecting them. Each of these faceless figures was armed, and stood there motionless. Each was dressed in the green mask, hood, and cloak which the Green Man had made notorious. The judge looked rapidly from one to another, seeking Luke.

While he was still eying them, Luke walked coolly into the room, dressed much like any of the other gentlemen at the ball. Passing by the cloaked sentinels, he went to where

Sir William Fossick was sitting and held a large, businesslike pistol to his fair head.

"Don't move, ladies and gentlemen," he commanded in his deep, resonant voice. "Or I shall be obliged to shoot poor Fossick."

)( )(
)){(CHAPTER NINETEEN }{ (
)( )(

KITTY SHRANK BACK in her chair, her heart pounding. There were some shrieks from the ladies and some angry cries of protest at the sight of the sentries at the door. Someone demanded to know if this was Denny's idea of a joke. On the dais Lord Comeragh had not moved at all. Only his bloated fingers, clutching and unclutching the gold knob of his stick, betrayed to Judge Moore that the old man was not oblivious to what was going on. Miss Amelia took one look at the cloaked, hooded figure that had appeared at her elbow, and clutched Lady Braxton's arm.

"L . . . look, Mama!"

"I am looking, Amelia," retorted Lady Braxton, the plumes on her silk turban appearing to tremble with indignation. "And no doubt, in time, we shall be given an explanation for this . . . this . . . outrage."

Luke's thin lips were seen to twitch slightly. He ordered the deputy sheriff to stand up.

"You'll hang for this," said Sir William coldly. "See if you don't."

"You think so, Fossick?"

"You and that brother of yours, you'll both hang. I've suspected that you'd a hand in this Green Man villainy, and now you've given me proof of it."

Luke said coolly, "I was responsible for some of it, certainly."

"Obliging of you to tell me so," snapped Sir William, gazing fearlessly back at his enemy. "You've saved me a deal of trouble."

Luke signaled to one of the cloaked sentinels, who was detailed to take Sir William to the only empty seat upon the dais and there to guard him. Luke also mounted the dais, and turned to face Lord Comeragh and his speechless companions who were seated there. "The Green Man," he said gravely, "is partly an imaginary figure, partly made up of the actions of several real persons. He has become a legend, not so much because a few men and women were saved from unjust imprisonment or death, but because the United agents feared him. They tried to stir up trouble, as you will know, and the Green Man several times discomfited them . . ."

"Ah," said Sir William sarcastically, "so the Green Man is a Loyalist, is he?"

"The Green Man's aim," said Luke, ignoring this outburst, "is to protect the innocent. He is not one, but several people—people who, in common with myself, saw a need to do something to protect the defenseless ones in this county. We tried to succor those who had become caught between two fires—between the growing violence of the United men on the one hand, and the sometimes more unbridled violence of the upholders of the law." This time he did turn to look at Sir William, and he then said calmly and deliberately, "The Green Man only helped the innocent . . ."

"What about Kelagher?" demanded Sir William. "He was a convicted murderer, Denny, and you know it."

"He was wrongly convicted, Fossick," replied Luke quietly. "You saw to that, did you not?"

"Ah! So that's your contention, is it, Denny? You are wrong, however. You made a mistake when you abducted Kelagher." Sir William's cold, blue, fearless gaze swept the room, resting on each of the silent sentinels who surrounded it. He was seen to smile. There were many there who said that William Fossick had shown no tremor of fear, not even when Denny's pistol had been pointing at his head. "You made a serious mistake then, Denny, and so did all the others. I'll hang every one of you," he added with savage clarity, "unless you lay down your arms this very instant. If you do that, I may be persuaded to be merciful . . ."

A harsh burst of laughter from one of the masked figures was the only answer he got to this overture. Luke said calmly, "We have little faith in your mercy, Fossick. And do not place any reliance on ours. I advise you not to move abruptly lest my friend beside you grows anxious."

"How much are you paying them to risk their necks, Denny?"

"Luke!" said Lady Braxton sharply. "Have you run mad?"

"Don't waste time bandying words with the feller, Euphemia," growled Lord Comeragh. "Let him tell us why he's here."

"Thank you, my lord," said Luke, inclining his head ironically in his kinsman's direction. "I am here to prove Paddy Kelagher's innocence, if I can."

"My lord," put in Sir William urgently, "Denny is a traitor. He has just admitted as much . . . Do not listen to him!"

"My boy," retorted the earl dryly, "I have found it best never to argue with a gun in my ribs. I recommend that course to you."

The judge knew that it was now too late to turn Luke from his chosen path, a path, in his opinion, which could only lead to disaster. Did Denny think he could herd his neighbors like sheep and be forgiven for it? There would be a reckoning for this night's work. Nothing of his thoughts showed in his face, however, as the ladies were given chairs to sit on, and the gentlemen (some protesting, but none of them with sufficient dash to do more than expostulate and threaten vengeance) were lined up like so many overdressed schoolboys. He saw Captain Dillon among them, his pink face as puzzled as ever.

Lord Comeragh feigned sleep, but he was furtively watching his dark, outrageous kinsman from under half-closed eyelids. He felt a reluctant admiration for Denny's audacity.

From her retreat at the side of the dais, half hidden by a bank of flowers, Kitty had eyes only for Luke. All the others in the crowded ballroom—the indignant, the terrified, the frankly curious—they might not have existed for her. Luke was the focus of her whole being. His harsh profile, his dark head, the small quirk of a suppressed smile which pulled at his mouth from time to time—these were reality for her. The others, even William Fossick in his chair above her, were of no account.

Luke started his story quietly. "This story concerns a lady called Katherine," he began.

There was a stir. There was scarcely anyone there who did not know of William Fossick's infatuation for Kitty Harcombe. "My dear Denny," said a voice plaintively, "we have heard that tale already."

"Bear with me, Esmond," returned Luke gently. "You have still some more to learn.

"Katherine was the only child of elderly parents. They were of the old faith; and as you will appreciate, to be of the old faith could be counted a disadvantage in worldly terms."

"Oh," remarked the man called Esmond, "so I was wrong, La Belle Harcombe was certainly never a papist!"

Luke waited for the ripple of laughter to die down. "I will not try to describe Katherine, except to say that she was very lovely. She heeded none of the men who admired her until one day she met . . . Harry." Luke looked about him at this point, his gaze passing from Lord Comeragh's ostensibly slumbering form, Sir William's disdainfully smiling face, and then on around the room. "Harry St. Dennis was a dashing fellow, as many of you will recall, and Katherine had never seen his like before. They fell in love. From the moment she saw Harry, there was no other man for her. She promised to marry him."

It was impossible to tell whether disbelief or astonishment predominated in the minds of Luke's audience, but that he had captured everyone's interest, there was no doubt. The earl opened his sandy-lashed eyes for a moment, like some basking monster, and then resolutely closed them again.

"So they were married," continued Luke, "though no one knew of it but the priest who married them and a kinsman who was a witness at the ceremony."

"Yourself, I suppose," put in the deputy sheriff. He added in a condescending tone, "Really, Denny, you'll have to do better than that!"

Luke glanced at him. "I mean to. Harry and Katherine were married, and a child was born to them in the city of

(242)

Dublin. And then, when Harry's regiment was sent to foreign parts, Katherine and the child returned home to her parents. You can imagine what rumor and speculation there was when Katherine reappeared after a long absence with a two-year-old son."

Lord Comeragh opened his eyes again. This time they remained open.

"Everyone waited to hear who the father was, but Katherine kept her secret. She was in an awkward situation, for she was prey, not only to the gossipmongers, but also to unwelcome admirers. Her husband was away for a long time, and one of her admirers declared that he wanted her and would wait no longer. Katherine resorted to all kinds of shifts and strategems to evade this man, but he wanted her and meant to have her. He issued an ultimatum. Either she came to him (and I must say, in fairness, that he offered her generous terms, and was even prepared for her to keep the boy) either she came to him or he would visit his wrath upon her parents. He was in a position to carry out this threat, and Katherine knew it. There were many ways in which a man of influence could bring about the ruin of poor people like Katherine's parents."

"Had she no friends who would stand by her?" demanded Mrs. Moore in a shocked voice.

"The only man who might have aided her was away. Her other champion, ma'am, was her grandfather's farm hand, a gentle, hulking creature with more brawn than brain . . ." Luke paused, and said deliberately, "Katherine's only other would-be champion was a man called Kelagher."

"Very touching, Denny," said Sir William. "The pity of it is that we are unable to believe you."

"Oh, come, Fossick," said Luke, letting his glittering, mocking gaze run over his victim. Never had he looked so assured, so dangerous. Miss Fossick, shrinking in her seat beside Mrs. Moore, thought he looked like a devil, the embodiment of her worst fears. "You'll not deny, Fossick," Luke said softly, "that you knew poor Katie Finn?"

Sir William hesitated. Then he said curtly, "I knew her. Yes."

"And you admired her excessively, did you not?"

Again he hesitated. The judge almost allowed himself to hope. A few more of these hesitations and Fossick would have them all wondering.

"Did you not, Fossick?"

At last Sir William was goaded into speech. "My lord, I protest!" he said loudly. "Denny's ambition, as you know, is to poison your mind against me. How am I best to answer him? If I keep silent, it makes me appear afraid. If I tell the truth, I am in danger of seeming less than perfect." He spread out his fine hands rather helplessly, and said in a disarming, rueful way, "It is true that I admired this farmer's daughter. She was a handsome female, and I was only one of many. To that much villainy I freely, though shame-facedly, confess. But as to the rest of it—that I threatened her or her parents—I did no such thing!"

"Bravo, my boy!" applauded Lord Comeragh, now fully awake and leaning on his cane. He glared at Luke. "Well, Denny. You hear that? If you think you can discredit William Fossick in my eyes, you're wasting your time."

"I think not, my lord," said Luke, smiling thinly. "Perhaps it will increase your interest if I tell you that you are now one of the chief characters in my story. Your grandson came back to Kilnabawn, if you remember, and though you could not know it, he was full of determination to tell you of his marriage to Katherine and of his son . . ."

"Moonshine! If Harry'd been wed, he'd never have feared to say so!"

Luke raised his brows and said mildly, "I think he feared you a little, my lord, and he feared, also, the effects of enraging you. You were in poor health at the time."

The earl was breathing heavily. He gasped out angrily, "If he'd had a son, he'd never have feared to tell me . . ."

"Then it's a pity that he did not," said Luke gravely, "for if he had, I believe that he would still be alive." He waited for a moment, but the earl could only stare at him blankly.

"The unwanted suitor did not know that Katherine was a married woman, either," he pursued crisply, "and he told Katherine that she must come to him that very week, or risk the consequences. She had not, until that time, dared to tell Harry of this other man, but at last she felt there was no alternative. She strove to make the tale as mild as she could. But Harry was outraged and would not be reasoned with. He rode out of the farmstead like a knight of old riding to avenge his lady's honor." He added dryly, "But unlike the best-prepared knights, he had omitted to arm himself, and had nothing but a stout stick and his fists with which to punish his wife's tormentor."

There was silence in the large ballroom. No shifting of feet, no clearing of throats or coughs broke the stillness. Lord Comeragh's bloodshot eyes were riveted upon his kinsman's face. His thick lips moved soundlessly.

Luke's voice was dry, devoid of expression. "The unwanted suitor had no warning. He was riding quietly along, when this young man set upon him like an avenging fury, challenging him with all his iniquities. Since he was skilled in the use of his fists, he should have dealt with Harry without trouble, but Harry was greatly enraged, and rage can lend strength to a man's arm. I do not know at what point the other man unsheathed the blade from a swordstick which he habitually carried with him . . ." Miss Fossick gave vent to a perfectly audible moan. There was a stir in the audience. Eveyone knew of the deputy sheriff's swordstick; he carried it with him whenever he rode alone.

Luke's voice broke through the murmurs. "With this blade he stabbed Harry St. Dennis to death. It was William Fossick who killed Harry St. Dennis, not Paddy Kelagher. William Fossick is the murderer, and it is time, high time, that the world should know him for what he is!"

There was a brief moment of complete silence. All eyes were riveted upon the old man in his chair, upon William Fossick sitting stiffly beside him and Luke Denny.

Then Lord Comeragh said, "And where's your proof of any of this, Denny?"

Lady Braxton said in a sharp voice, "Yes, indeed! What you say is absolutely incredible!"

Sir William burst out laughing. His laugh, boisterous, shocking in its unexpectedness, seemed at first to convulse him utterly. After a moment, however, he managed to say, "Lady Braxton, I thank you! Incredible is just what it seemed to me, but I had not dared to hope that you would see through Denny's affecting tale. You told it uncommonly well, my dear Denny," he added kindly, "but evidently her Ladyship was not deceived, and perhaps there may be others among us who will require something in the nature of evidence before they condemn me."

"Aye, Denny," snapped the earl, "where is your evidence?"

"And why," put in Sir William, smiling, "did you wait all these months before informing us of all these startling facts? Could it have anything to do with your young brother's present predicament?"

To Kitty's dismay, Luke did not answer. He just stood

there, looking gravely at Sir William. Surely Kitty's unnoticed gaze beseeched him, surely he could bluff a little? There was a general hubbub as several of his earlier auditors demanded that he should substantiate his words.

It was Sir William who stayed the tumult. He held up a white hand and said pleasantly, "Pray, let Denny speak, gentlemen. I am all curiosity, for if there is a grain of established fact among all this mountain of slander and surmise, we should, I think, be permitted to share it." There was no doubt then that the laughter was on the deputy sheriff's side. Even those who did not much like him had to admit to a surge of admiration for his coolness. He was at ease, unperturbed, despite the masked desperado at his side. Sir William, and not Luke, seemed to be in charge of the proceedings. "Tell me, Denny," he added cheerfully, "why have you waited so long if you have known me to be Harry St. Dennis's murderer all this time?"

"I had my reasons," said Luke shortly.

"You had your reasons," echoed Sir William silkily. "You are desperate, are you not, Denny?" He turned in his chair to address Lord Comeragh, and said in a calm, reasoning tone, "My lord, I submit to you that Denny is trying to divert attention from his brother, and from his own guilt. He wants you to believe that I killed Harry. I, who loved him . . ." For a moment it was seen that Sir William was almost overcome with emotion. ". . . who loved him like the brother I never had." He straightened in his chair and his voice recovered its ringing tone. "It is a false slander, my lord—and a vicious and cruel one! I would give my own life, and willingly, if I could bring Harry back to us."

"And Harry's wife and son?" put in Luke. "Would you bring them back too?"

"Harry had no wife, Denny."

(247)

"Harry did indeed have a wife and she perished, as you know, on the night your men set fire to the Finns' farm. You made very sure, didn't you, Fossick, that there would be no living witnesses to your criminal act?"

"Oh, so I am to be accused of that?" remarked the deputy sheriff in a resigned, partly humorous voice. "What next, I wonder?"

"Fossick's right," put in the earl suddenly. "Harry could not have been married to this woman. He could never have hidden it all those years . . ." He began to breathe in a labored, wheezing way. "And, indeed, why should he have wanted to keep it from me?"

"My lord," said Sir William in a low, concerned voice, "pray do not excite yourself. You will only oblige Denny if you make yourself ill again."

His Lordship chuckled in a ferocious, catarrhal fashion and said, "There's more life in me than any of you think! But you'd not be sorry to see me dead, would you, Denny?"

Luke said, "No. Why should I be, indeed?"

"Well, that's frank, at all events," retorted Lord Comeragh. "You may claim to have known my grandson, Denny, for since the boy is dead, no one can prove anything to the contrary. But if you knew him well, you would know this . . ." He paused, then said slowly and deliberately, "If Harry had a son, and if that son had been born in wedlock, he would have brought him to me."

"You forget," returned Luke, "that Katie Finn, the mother, was a papist."

"Even . . . even if she were," retorted Lord Comeragh, "I would still have acknowledged the child."

"And would you have brought him up at Kilnabawn, my lord?" asked Luke, sounding as if he found this hard to believe.

"Naturally. And Harry would have known it."

"And would you have allowed Harry's wife to bring up her son as a member of the Roman Catholic faith?"

The answer came like an explosion. "Harry's son? A papist? Certainly not!"

Luke nodded. "Ah! Then Harry was right. He feared that you would never allow it, and to Katie, who was a devout Catholic, it seemed preferable that her son should grow up poor and nameless than that he should be raised at Kilnabawn in a heretic faith."

"The hussy! So it was she who hid the boy!"

"She did, my lord. Katie was gentle, but she had an iron will under that dreamy manner of hers, as Fossick, if he were disposed to be frank, could tell you. And though Harry wanted to bring her to you before he went away, Katie would not allow it. She would do anything else he wished, she said, but not that. So Harry went abroad, and Katie had her way. It was not easy for her, I think, and there must have been times when she regretted her decision. She certainly began to regret it bitterly when William Fossick made her the object of his attentions."

"Nonsense, Denny! She liked my attentions very well."

Luke ignored the laughter. His eyes were fixed on Lord Comeragh's face, and the earl looked steadily back at him. "I think she would have relented in the end and allowed the boy to go to Kilnabawn; but Harry was murdered, my lord, and Katie knew of his death before she was shot through the lungs by a militiaman's bullet. As she lay dying, my lord, she made me promise that I would keep the boy safe, and that I would bring him up as a good Catholic. Until today I have kept both those promises. Now I can no longer count on keeping the boy safe, so I have decided"—briefly he turned his dark head and nodded to the sentinel who stood by the main door—"I have decided to bring him here to you."

There was a stir as the door opened and Father James came into the ballroom, leading Shamus Finn by the hand. The little boy was dressed with unusual neatness in nankeen trousers and a spotless shirt. His red hair, though still curling irrepressibly, was combed back from his brow, and as he was led into the crowded room, he gazed around him with solemn and unabashed curiosity. When he saw who was standing on the dais, he broke away from the priest's restraining hand and ran to Luke, tugged on his arm and reached up to whisper something urgently in his ear. Luke leaned down to hear what the child had to say, and then straightened up, saying mildly, "Yes. Later, you may . . ." He glanced down at the child and turned him toward Lady Braxton and Lord Comeragh, who was leaning forward in his chair, devouring Shamus's face with his bloodshot eyes, and said firmly, "Meanwhile you must make your bow to Lady Braxton and to his Lordship."

Shamus complied, staring fascinated at the plumes on Lady Braxton's turban as he did so, while Luke said with a wry smile, "I must ask you to excuse his manners, ma'am, but he has been waiting in the dining room, and apparently the sight of so many jellies and creams has quite overwhelmed him . . ."

Lord Comeragh leaned even farther forward and said in a peremptory grating tone, "Come here, boy."

Shamus glanced at Luke, who nodded, and he went forward a little timidly. The earl laid a hand on the child's shoulder and seemed for the moment at a loss as to what to say to him. He struggled for breath. Finally he said, "What's yer name, eh?"

"Shamus, sir . . ."

"Shamus . . . ? And what else?"

"Shamus Finn, sir . . ."

"Just that, they call you, do they?"

Shamus nodded his red head. He gazed back at the earl without fear but with a good deal of astonishment. He could not at all imagine why this stout gentleman wanted to ask him his name, and why he should have been brought to this vast, grand house in the middle of the night. However, Luke was there behind him and he had already calculated that it was at least four hours past his bedtime. He did not believe that even Mary had ever been allowed to stay up so late. He wished that the stout gentleman would not grasp his shoulder so tightly with his hot fingers.

The earl was gazing at Shamus, searching his face. Suddenly he said, "So you've been guzzling my guests' supper, eh?"

"Oh, no, sir," replied Shamus in an injured tone. "Father said that I might not do so until I had been invited . . ."

"Father?" said the earl quickly. He glanced up, saw the black-clad priest standing at the foot of the dais, and added with a snort, "Oh, he said that, did he? And d'yer mean to tell me, boy," he went on, taking his hand off Shamus's shoulder and poking him in the ribs with a sort of lumbering joviality, "d'yer mean to tell me that you didn't contrive to sneak just a taste for yerself?"

Shamus, relieved that he was no longer being grasped so convulsively, looked at the stout man for a moment and began to hope that he had found an ally. His mouth began to curl upward, to broaden into an urchin grin. "Well, just a small bit, sir, when no one was looking . . ."

The earl chuckled. "And you'd like some more, eh?"

Shamus nodded vehemently.

"Then be off and satisfy your appetite, boy . . ."

Shamus turned to go with some alacrity, but he came back a moment later and said, "Please, sir . . ."

(251)

"What d'yer want now?"

Shamus's clear, piping voice was more confident now. He said beseechingly, "Could Father have some supper too?"

"Aye, feed him too, if you've a mind to it. P'raps that way you'll save yourself a wigging."

CHAPTER TWENTY

THERE WERE SOME SMILES among the company as Shamus and the priest went out, but when they had gone, Lord Comeragh's face had resumed its grimmest, most belligerent aspect. He turned to Luke and said in a shocked, incredulous whisper, "You are trying to tell me that the boy is Harry's son . . . and . . . that you kept him from me, Denny? You kept him!"

"Now, look here, Denny . . ." broke in Sir William hotly.

"Hush, Fossick! Let him speak," growled the earl.

Luke said, "I kept him from you, my lord, and would do so again. I gave my word to Katie, for one thing, and I cannot think that your Lordship will be an ideal guardian." The earl, fighting for breath and wrestling with a variety of powerful emotions, was for the moment speechless, and Luke went on with renewed gravity. "While Fossick believed that the boy had perished with his mother, he was safe enough at Dennystown. But last night, by chance, Fossick and the boy came face to face."

The earl seemed to drag his eyes away from Luke's face. He said sternly, "William, you actually saw this child and said nothing of it to me?"

"Why, certainly," Sir William retorted, as though the matter were of small account, "for why should I suppose that Katie Finn's bastard was of interest to your Lordship? And as for this freakish story about Harry being the brat's father, don't you believe it, my lord!"

The earl said thoughtfully, "There's just a look of Harry when he smiles . . ."

"Denny has conditioned your mind to look for a resemblance, my lord," retorted Sir William. "Ten to one, even Katie did not know who the father was, and when Denny offers us stronger proof than a crop of red hair and a pair of appealing blue eyes, I shall begin to take an interest. It was a good stroke, Denny," he added, smiling coldly at Luke, "to bring the child here and to appeal to our sentiments. But it was not, to my mind, quite good enough. If Katie Finn was a married woman, there will have been marriage lines. Where are they? It is not enough that you say you witnessed the ceremony."

Luke did not at once reply.

"You see," pursued Sir William triumphantly, "he has no proof! The whole thing is a tissue of lies from beginning to end, and let us hope," he added with a well-executed yawn, "that Denny has nearly come to an end of his farrago. For my part, I have long ago lost interest in both Katie Finn and her child."

"Then why," demanded Luke in a voice which cut like a

knife, "did you turn Dennystown upside down in search of him this morning?"

Sir William said lightly, his eyes pale and steady, "Why? To teach your household that it does not do to play games with me."

"And Paddy Joe, whose neck you had broken? Was he being taught a lesson, too?"

"That was a mistake, Denny. You know that, and I regret it."

"Ah. A mistake," murmured Luke, regarding Sir William through his glass as though he were of peculiar interest. "And you regret it, do you? I think, Fossick, that you regret even more deeply that Shamus St. Dennis did not perish with his mother."

"For shame!" cried Sir William sharply. "How dare you call the child by that name? Have you no thought for the pain you must cause . . ."

"Well, I cannot blame you if you do not like it, Fossick," said Luke, smiling grimly. "You are an ambitious man, and it must have been bitter for you to find a small boy still standing between you and the wealth and power you had come to count on. A bitter blow, Fossick, worse by far than the mere death by strangulation of an old man."

Sir William said curtly, "That child is a bastard, Denny, as all the world knows. And as to Duffy killing your groom, it was a shocking thing and he will be punished for it. If the old man had kept still, he would not have died."

"I wonder," countered Luke, still smiling in that mirthless, ice-cold way, "if you will be able to keep still when you have a noose around your neck."

Miss Fossick suddenly cried out in protest. She tried to rise to her feet, but Mrs. Moore restrained her.

Luke said clearly and calmly, "Rest easy, Miss Fossick, I do not mean to cheat the hangman of his purse a second

(255)

time. If your brother is hanged by the neck, ma'am, it will be after he is condemned by a court of law as a murderer, and there will be no Green Man to take his part."

Miss Fossick gazed at Luke as a rabbit might gaze at a stoat, unable to tear her eyes from his dark, accusing face.

Luke looked away from her and said curtly, "Now, Fossick, you all but tore Dennystown to pieces today, searching for a small boy who goes by the name of Shamus Finn. You failed to find him. What did you do then?"

"Do then?" Sir William appeared to stifle a yawn. "Why, I thought no more about it."

'You took no steps to find the child?'

'None.'

"You are quite sure of this, Fossick?"

Sir William sighed. "Quite sure, Denny," he replied wearily.

"Very well." Once more Luke made a sign and Matthew Cullen was hustled into the room. He was pale and had a bruise on the side of his face. Luke turned to Miss Fossick, and said quite gently, "Have you seen this man before, ma'am?"

Miss Fossick nodded. A painful tide of color began to seep under her mottled skin.

"And when was that, ma'am?"

This time she gasped out that it had been in the shrubbery that very evening that she had seen him.

"In which shrubbery, ma'am?"

She licked her lips. "At the Lodge. He . . . that man . . . was coming to see . . . my brother." Her voice faded away on a trembling sigh, as though the effort of speech had tired her inexpressibly.

"Thank you," said Luke. He turned to Cullen and said curtly, "Tell us, Cullen. What business had you with Sir William this evening that brought you creeping through his shrubbery?"

"My lord," Sir William protested in the tone of one who is on the verge of losing his patience, "this man is a spy, an informer. Don't believe all he says, I beg of you."

"Why did you go to the Lodge, Cullen?"

Cullen said sullenly, "His honor was after owing me money."

"Money for what?" Cullen did not answer, so Luke said, "Was it, perhaps, your reward for leading Sir William to the Green Man?"

Cullen nodded and muttered something.

"Speak up," said Luke inexorably. "We all want to hear what you have to say. Did you, or did you not, lead Sir William to suppose that my brother was the Green Man?"

Cullen said defensively, "I was after thinking he was, myself. But I'll tell you this," he added in an aggrieved tone, "that if I'd known what they was going to do to Mister Mick in prison, I'd never have given him up! Not for twice one thousand pounds!"

"A thousand pounds?" Luke allowed this information to sink in before he continued. "Tell the gentlemen, will you, of the other little commission you were entrusted with this evening?"

Again Sir William broke in to protest, this time more sharply. "This man's testimony is wholly unreliable. Given a sufficient bribe, he will say anything. He's not to be believed, I assure you, my lord."

"Then why," inquired Luke mildly, "did you believe him when he told you that my brother was the Green Man?"

"Because I'd suspected it all along."

"And another thing," Luke added. "Why, if you regard this man as a miscreant, did you offer him the sum of five hundred pounds to take young Shamus St. Dennis to America? If you are no longer interested in what becomes of the child, it seems a steep price to pay."

"St. Dennis?" echoed Cullen, flicking a furtive and startled glance at the earl, then back to Luke. "So them papers in the chest . . . they was . . ."

"Sir! My lord!" Sir William said loudly. "How many more calumnies must we listen to? I daresay that Denny can summon up any number of witnesses, but if none of them is more trustworthy than this man Cullen, you may be sure that they can be browbeaten or bribed into saying anything."

Crouching beside Mrs. Moore on a small gilt sofa near the dais, Miss Fossick heard the note of desperation creeping into her brother's voice. She had been afraid of him, yet for so long afraid, too, for what might befall him that fear and dread had become a part of her. Yet when William spoke thus, with a voice growing overloud and edged with panic, something inside her trembling body grew suddenly cold and deadly calm.

Until that moment she had been mesmerised by Luke's face, caught up in a paralysis of horror, certain in her terrified mind that Luke Denny knew of William's guilt and that he meant to expose him before them all. Ever since the dreadful night that William had come to her, bloody and distraught, she had known in her heart that Luke Denny was the man to be feared.

She rose to her feet. Mrs. Moore laid a restraining hand upon her arm, but she ignored it. She had to get to William.

She was forestalled. Kitty Harcombe walked gracefully onto the dais in front of her, obscuring her view of her brother.

Miss Fossick had no means of knowing that Kitty was still clutching a small pistol in one hand. She would not have cared if she had known it. She was beyond fear of such things, being possessed at that moment by a feeling of burning re-sentment at the unfairness of it all, and above all by her dislike and mistrust of Kitty Harcombe. She it was, more than Luke Denny, who was to blame for their predicament: this siren who had almost succeeded in marrying William, and who by coming into Tipperary had brought Luke Denny and William together.

Kitty said in her clear drawling voice, "No one can bribe or browbeat me, William. So may I be permitted to add my evidence to all the others?" She curtsyed to the goggling Lady Braxton and to Lord Comeragh, smiled down at the deputy sheriff, who still sat imprisoned on his chair, and repeated, "May I?"

"Lady Kitty!" said Luke sternly, "Keep out of this, if you please."

She turned her bright head slowly and gave him a limpid look. "I do not please, sir."

Miss Fossick witnessed this exchange of glances, and was sure, as she had suspected for the past few days, that Luke and Kitty were as one, joined in their wicked conspiracy against William. She began to move forward.

Kitty saw her coming. The sight gave her an unpleasant shock, for there was a look in Miss Fossick's eyes that she did not at all like. Those eyes were fastened with painful inten-sity upon her own face. Involuntarily she took a step back-ward.

"This is your fault, Lady Kitty!" said Miss Fossick hoarsely. "If you had not come here, we should have been safe. But you wanted all along to come, didn't you? You wanted to destroy us."

"No," said Kitty, stepping backward again, "no, ma'am."

It was at this moment that Kitty felt Sir William's fingers enclose her wrist like an iron band, twisting it cruelly and wresting the pistol from her grasp. Something cold pressed against her neck, and she felt him stand up behind her. The masked man who was guarding him told him sharply to sit down, but Sir William merely said in a loud voice, "Keep still! Keep still or I shall shoot her!"

Miss Fossick's blue eyes looked as if they would start out of her head, and she gave a strangled moan and fainted. No one seemed to notice her. Everyone else was frozen into a startled tableau.

"Now, Denny," said Sir William, "it is my turn to give the orders, and if anyone is so foolish as to disobey me, I shall not hesitate to dispose of this interfering female."

"Let her go, Fossick," said Luke quietly. "I am the man you want. It is to me that you owe your defeat."

Sir William laughed. His eyes were blazing and intent as he ordered all the masked men to drop their weapons to the ground. One by one they complied, and then he ordered all the company to move to one side of the room.

"No, not you, Denny," he added, turning to his taut, silent enemy. "Stay where you are. You flatter yourself if you think you will defeat me, you know. I never let anyone defeat me. Harry thought to oppose me, and I had to kill him. It was better so. He would always have stood in my way." Again he laughed. "And Katie Finn, who thought she could refuse me —she learned better, too."

He was all the while propelling Kitty across the room to the half-open door, holding her before him as he backed away from the other occupants of the ballroom. "I am about to take my leave of you, but in case you are thinking of pursuing me, I warn you that I shall shoot her Ladyship if I hear anyone following me."

"You'll not get far with a female for company," said Luke evenly. "You'll stand a better chance on your own, Fossick."

"Ah," retorted Sir William, smiling coldly. "But I have hopes of enjoying her Ladyship's company where I am going." Kitty moved convulsively in his hold. "No. Do not struggle, ma'am. You are mine now, as you should have been from the start."

"The house is surrounded by my people," said Luke. "You'll never contrive to leave it if there are two of you."

For a moment Kitty felt the deputy sheriff's steely grip tighten. She almost cried out with the pain of it. Then he said coldly, "You're bluffing, Denny."

"You think so, Fossick?"

Sir William began to back through the door, pulling Kitty after him. "I mean to call your bluff, however," and with these words he brought his pistol past Kitty's head and fired straight at Luke. Kitty saw Luke stagger, and she screamed and dragged at Sir William's arm as he raised the weapon to fire again. For some reason there was no second deafening explosion in her ear. She heard Sir William utter an oath, saw Luke coming on in a lunging run, his face contorted. Then Sir William raised his pistol and struck her hard on the side of the head. Freed of Kitty's convulsive grasp, he turned and ran down the wide, flower-flanked gallery, with Luke after him.

Kitty was on her knees, blinded by the agony of that blow. When her vision cleared, she raised her head and peered down the gallery, only to find that several gentlemen were tearing by her, shouting and exclaiming. She could see no sign of Luke, no sign of Sir William, only a gesticulating group of men at the end of the gallery. She closed her eyes, overcome by a spasm of nausea. More people ran by, and painfully, slowly, she dragged herself to her feet, clutching at the door, then to a chair. Leaning weakly against the wall, or grasping at a pillar or whatever was near enough to give her support, she finally groped her way drunkenly to where they all were. The red-hot hammer in her head gave her no respite, and when she gained the top of the gallery stairs, she was spent.

She sank to her knees again, and raising her head to look once more at all those backs above her, she saw the group waver and part. Luke came through, slowly, as though he were exceedingly weary. There was a drawn look about his face and his coat was torn. As he saw Kitty, she gazed painfully at him and began to pull herself upright, her lips working soundlessly and her eyes asking the question that she was too weak to put into words.

Luke nodded and came over to her. "It's all right," he said firmly, drawing her to her feet and holding her as she swayed in his grasp. "He only scratched me, you know. Nothing to worry about."

"And W . . . William?"

He nodded again. "The sheriff's men have him. Come, ma'am. It is all over."

CHAPTER TWENTY-ONE

IT WAS ALL OVER. There was a tendency, at first, to try to put the Green Man back on his pedestal, to make a hero of him again. These efforts were not wholly successful. Ladies who had once sighed ecstatically at the thought of the Green Man carrying them off, rescuing them from a fate worse than death, now found it a trifle less romantic. To be saved in however dramatic a fashion by stout Father James was somehow not quite as it should be. And no lady of sensibility would wish to be carried off by one of those malodorous tinkers. They might have worked themselves into a state of worship for Mr. Denny, who had brought about Sir William's downfall. But as soon as Mick was found to be unlikely to die of his wounds, the inconsiderate Mr. Denny carried him off to Dennystown. Neither of them was seen again for some time. All in all, it was dispiriting, and before long the forthcoming point-to-point races had replaced the Green Man as the main topic of interest.

As for Kitty, she was slow to recover from her experiences. It seemed that her first few days in County Tipperary had at last done what years of racketing in London had failed to do. She was quite worn down. She could not sleep, or if she did manage to get to sleep, she woke up again, sweating and shaking all over as if she had an ague. Mrs. Moore, to whose house Judge Moore had taken her on the night of Sir William's capture, said that it was no wonder. She must stay in bed, with Martha to care for her; and after a week, Mrs. Moore assured her, she would be feeling quite the thing again.

A week passed. Kitty found herself no longer sick and dizzy, but she did not feel at all the thing. For it was becoming more and more apparent that it was all over for her, too.

She might once have entertained hopes, and imagined that there had been signs of tenderness and admiration in Luke's dark eyes. Indeed, she had entertained these hopes most eagerly, but as the days passed, a number of things gradually prevailed upon her reluctant understanding, and she was forced to see that it had all been in her own too hopeful mind. When Luke had handed her, half fainting, into the judge's keeping on that dreadful night, riding off immediately without so much as another glance, he had evidently considered that his responsibility for her was at an end. He had washed his hands of her, without regret or compunction. By the time that two weeks had passed, Kitty had come to accept this disagreeable fact as the truth.

At first she had expected him to call. But he did not call. She heard tell of his doings from several sources, but never a word was said about him asking after her health or inquiring for her in any way. He had evidently forgotten all about her, and Martha had contributed to Kitty's growing hopelessness by assuring her that everyone at Dennystown had been glad to see the last of the Harcombes. Apparently the general feeling was that Kitty's coming had been to blame for the whole disastrous sequence of events, and that her going was a good riddance.

Martha thought it disgraceful that those papist good-for-nothings should dare to cast aspersions upon her mistress, and (as Kitty could all too clearly imagine) Martha herself had done her bit to make things worse. She had left Dennystown with Robert, but not, she said proudly, without telling them what she thought of them all!

So they were glad to be rid of her? Nevertheless, Kitty was still eager to learn how the Dennys were going on. She heard that Mick was recovering and that Luke's wound had proved to be a mere graze on his arm. Mrs. Moore was the kindest and most garrulous of hostesses, and she kept Kitty supplied with information about all the local trivialities. She could not understand Luke's absence either, and kept remarking with unwelcome frequency upon his offhand ways. But, as she said, Luke Denny's manners had never been quite what one would look for in a gentleman. The judge was an admirer of his, she knew, but she herself had always regarded him as far too careless and neglectful of the proprieties. She could not feel at all sorry that Mr. Denny had stayed away. Still, one might have expected him to write a note of inquiry, just to ask how Kitty was going on after her horrid adventures. Did Kitty herself not feel that he was showing a good deal too little concern?

Kitty, by this time feeling stronger and no ·longer prey to weak outbursts of tears, managed to laugh it all off creditably enough. There was not much need to dissemble with Mrs. Moore. That kindly lady, though passionately interested and communicative about her neighbors, her neighbors' children, their dogs, their horses, and all there was about them, was not at all observant. She prosed on happily, delighted with her captive audience, and she would have been totally astonished if she had known that she was causing pain.

She was, of course, eager for anything that Kitty could tell her about Shamus. Such a dear little boy, she said. She wished that Mr. Denny had not taken him away from her so soon. But as for his going to live with Lord Comeragh, there had had to be a put-off. The old man had taken one of his bad turns on the day after the ball. Mrs. Moore eyed Kitty rather apprehensively as it struck her that the ball at Kilnabawn was not a happy subject to raise. "I daresay," she added hurriedly, "that Mr. Denny is relieved. He will not wish to part with the boy after caring for him for all these months. And although it must be a marvelous thing for the child . . ."

"Oh, no!" put in Kitty. "It makes me shudder to think of little Shamus going to live in that great formal place."

Mrs. Moore agreed with her readily enough. "I was thinking more of the material advantages," she explained. "After all, as the future Earl of Comeragh, it is only fitting that the child should begin to learn of his inheritance. Lord Comeragh is his natural and lawful guardian now, for you know, my dear, they found a box with the marriage lines and all Harry's letters in it. The whole story was true, after all."

"I still think that Shamus is young to be sent to Kilnabawn. Mr. Denny should make a push to keep him."

"Yes, dear," said Mrs. Moore, forever agreeable, "and I daresay that Mr. Denny would like to. Much as Lord Comeragh deplores the thought of his grandson being raised as a

Catholic, Mr. Denny will think it just as shocking that he should not be. Those well-born Catholics are as proud and exclusive as any class of people in the land, my dear. They keep themselves to themselves, even if it is to their disadvantage. They would never dream of marrying into a Protestant family, not even if they stood to gain a fortune by it, or if it had been a duke's daughter. They consider mixed marriages as even more shocking than we might do. Mark my words, even your Mr. Denny will choose a good Catholic bride when the time comes and have himself half a dozen children in as many years. These things are sometimes arranged for them in the cradle."

Mrs. Moore noticed that Kitty was looking rather startled, and she added, smiling, "I can see that your acquaintance with that gentleman makes it hard for you to think of him as a sober married man, but I assure you that I know better. And as for Mr. Denny thinking that Shamus is bettering himself by going to live at Kilnabawn, it will be no such thing. More than likely he will be regretting that he ever disclosed the little boy's identity."

"Most likely," said Kitty bleakly.

So that was it. Luke had not been to see her because he simply did not wish to become involved. Perhaps he, too, had felt that strong undertow of attraction, and being more sensible and clear-sighted than herself, had known full well where it might lead. Perhaps, with the high-mindedness which he was always so determined to disclaim, he wished to spare her the insult of a dishonorable proposal? She wondered sadly whether she would have been able to refuse any proposal from Luke, if he had made her one.

Well, he had not done so, and at the end of fifteen days, there really did not seem to be any reason to suppose that he ever would. She began to make plans for her return to Lon-

(267)

don, and this time both the judge and Mrs. Moore declared their intention of escorting her. She was secretly rather glad to have their company on the tedious journey, and after a few protestations, she threw up her hands in mock despair and gave all the arrangements into their keeping.

She was sitting in her bedchamber one sunny morning, watching Martha folding her dresses into a trunk, when there came a knock at the door. Martha went to see who it was, and came back to say, with a certain arch innuendo, that a gentleman and a young lady had called. Would her Ladyship see them?

Her Ladyship, trying to stifle a sudden and quite unfounded surge of optimism, sped down the stairs.

At first the drawing room looked empty. Then there was a rush of feet and Shamus and Mary literally hurled themselves at her. When she had extricated herself from their enthusiastic embraces, she said, "What a charming surprise! Do you know, I had almost given up hope of seeing you again, for I am leaving tomorrow."

"That is what Luke told us, Lady Kitty," said Mary. "So we've brought you something . . . a keepsake to take back to London."

With a certain amount of giggling and rustling of paper they presented their gift, which was a large watercolor sketch of Mount Comeragh Castle. The colors were crude, and the painting bore unmistakable marks of some painstaking erasures and corrections. Nevertheless, the subject was clear enough. It was bordered by a circle of green leaves.

"To remind you," Mary informed her eagerly, "that it was at the Castle that you first met the Green Man." Shamus made a hurried sign, and she added chidingly, "Oh, I know that Luke does not like us to talk of it, but

Lady Kitty will not mind. Do you like the picture, ma'am? I painted it myself."

"You never did so!" exclaimed Kitty, suitably amazed and admiring. She smiled down at Mary and said very gently, "You could not have given me anything I could like more. I shall look at it when I am homesick for Ireland."

"But you will come back. Of course you will!" said Mary, rather anxiously. "Surely you will?"

Kitty's green eyes were very bright. "Why, I don't think so. London is a hard place to break away from, you know, and once I am there I shall be swept into so many routs and parties that I shall scarcely have time to turn around. It is always so. But you will come to London, Mary, when you are older. You will make your curtsy at one of the drawing rooms, and you will go to balls and break all the young men's hearts. And I, I shall be an old dowager by then and shall stare at you through my lorgnette."

"Just like Luke when he is being odious," put in Mary with a giggle. "I can imagine the two of you."

"Oh, your brother will be married by then, with dozens of children of his own."

Mary grinned mischievously. "I don't suppose he will ever grow out of being odious. He sends his regards to you, Lady Kitty, but he would not get out of the curricle. He said that he did not want to leave the horses. Come and speak to him, Lady Kitty. Do!"

But Kitty declined, and since they had obviously been strictly limited to five minutes, they soon embraced her and went away. She was left alone in Mrs. Moore's drawing room, holding the picture in her hand. If Luke did not wish to see her, she told herself fiercely, he need not. Did he imagine that she would positively pursue him?

"Do you like your picture, ma'am?" inquired Luke behind her.

Kitty did not turn around. "The children have already gone out to you, Mr. Denny," she said distantly. "Didn't you see them?"

With one hand he took the picture from her and with the other he turned her round to face him. She could not prevent him looking at her, she supposed, but she saw no need to meet his penetrating, searching gaze. With lowered head and a voice which had grown disconcertingly husky, she said, "They were terrified of keeping you waiting, of course. Pray go quickly. It is not fair to keep them after telling them so strictly."

He had somehow, unfairly, possessed himself of her hands. Her pulses began to race in a most disconcerting manner, and while she was trying to steady her breath, he said, "Why are you so anxious to send me away?"

She said foolishly, "You were only looking for the children . . . weren't you?"

"No."

"Well," she went on, finding it necessary to say something, however idiotic, "and how is . . . Mick and Miss Biddy . . . and everyone . . . ? I have been so curious to know how you have all been going on."

"Have you?" She thought he sounded amused, but when she glanced at him, she saw that his dark face was perfectly grave. He added quietly, "I, too, have been thinking of you."

"Oh?"

"I've come to ask your advice, ma'am."

"Oh?"

In that same grave, thoughtful tone he said, "I am thinking of taking a wife."

"Oh!" said Kitty for the third time. Her voice seemed to

have got caught in her throat and was scarcely more than a shaking sigh. Knowing that this would not do, she managed to say primly, "I trust that you will be happy."

"Oh, I certainly trust so," agreed Luke cordially.

"And . . . and . . ." The stiff little voice seemed somehow unlike her own, but it was better than stunned silence. She said doggedly, "Please give your bride . . . your bride-to-be my . . . best wishes."

"That will be difficult," returned Luke. "I have no idea, yet, whether she will agree to marry me. Do you think I'll make a good husband, ma'am?"

This was too much. She said furiously, "How should I know? I daresay you will not care what kind of husband you may make! No doubt you will find someone whom you can bully and browbeat, who will not dare to speak . . . until . . ." She had cast aside all caution, and no longer cared if he thought it strange that her eyes should be filled with angry tears. She glared up into his face, and suddenly caught her breath on a strangled sob. He was laughing down at her, smiling into her blurring eyes in such a way that a warm trembling took possession of her body.

"You told me once," he said, no longer laughing but still looking at her in that unfair, heart-shaking way. "Do you remember? You told me once that you would never consent to marry me. Did you mean it? I rather hoped that you did not."

She found herself mesmerised, unable to break her gaze from his intent, warm regard. She said, not daring to believe the message it held, "What are you saying?"

"I am asking you to marry me." He smiled at her look of consternation. "It's quite the thing to do, you know, and even a farouche fellow like myself has to follow the mode at times like these."

(271)

"Tiresome for you," she drawled, still distrustful of his gravity, "but what is a lady to say in reply? Shall I be overcome by your offer and say that it is too sudden?"

He said nothing, and since she felt unable to sustain that tender, shining look of his any longer, she said somewhat indignantly, "And it is certainly more than sudden, Mr. Denny! You have not written or been near me since you threw me at poor Judge Moore two weeks ago! I may tell you that we leave for England tomorrow. Are you trying to make my experiences of Ireland complete by giving me a chance to boast of a proposal of marriage? What a blow it would be if I were to accept you!"

He said curtly, "When you have finished being nonsensical, ma'am, perhaps you will give me an answer. Will you marry me, or will you not? I don't mean to moon around you forever, waiting for an answer."

"No!" she flashed at him waspishly. "We must not keep your horses waiting, must we?"

"Kitty," he said, dangerously quiet, "there are limits to my patience. I am perfectly serious, and if you do not mean to have me, then say so. I believe you are capable of giving me an honest answer, whatever your reputation may be to the contrary."

She looked at him, her gravity suddenly matching his own. She said, rather sadly, "If you are serious, if you are really serious, you must see that my reputation alone would be a bar to our marriage."

"I think your reputation is more than half an invention of your own, ma'am, so we will discount it. What other reasons can you give me for refusing?"

"I . . . I am not a Catholic," she said unsteadily, trying to overcome the sensation that she was dreaming and would soon wake up. Recalling what Mrs. Moore had told her, she

(272)

said resolutely, "You know very well that you should marry someone of your own faith."

He shrugged. "That's for me to say. Do you find it intolerable, the thought of marrying a papist? I could understand it if you did. There will be difficulties." He had moved away from her and was standing at the far side of the fireplace, regarding her gravely and searchingly. "But I don't think the difficulties will be insurmountable. What other reasons, ma'am?"

"I'm told they look on me as a murderess at Dennystown," she told him, wincing inwardly as she recalled Martha's words. "They do, I promise you!" she protested as he looked unbelieving and almost indulgent. "Martha told me so. Perhaps you do not hear all that is said."

"Fustian," he said impatiently, taking a pinch of snuff and waiting with apparent nonchalance for her next pretext for refusing his offer. "What next?"

She said pettishly, "I do not like the horrid way you spill snuff all down yourself, for another thing! I do not believe that you take the least pride in your appearance! Now, what do you think you're about, Mr. Denny?" she protested urgently as he swooped down upon her and lifted her right off the ground, twirling her round with a shout of laughter.

He set her down again, still laughing, and said, "You will have to marry me, my darling, if only to reform my slovenly ways. And for other reasons, too! I mean to have you, for one thing, and I can't live without you. Even if you've a disgust of my person," he added, kissing her lips in the manner of one who means to stand no more nonsense, "you know that you belong to me, and I to you. You knew it from the first, didn't you?"

She nodded, and he kissed her again in a far more leisurely fashion. Presently she broke away from him, and said with a dazed but desperate attempt at firmness, "Mr. Denny, this is all madness. One of us must try to be sensible."

"But I have not the smallest wish to be sensible," he retorted. "Come here!"

She shook her head. "There are so many things to be thought of. There is Robert."

"To be sure, there is Robert," he agreed, still waiting for her to come back to him, "but I don't wish to think of him now . . ."

"There are so many risks and pitfalls," she insisted as he came toward her, wearing that glittering, undermining look. "It would be taking a chance."

"And what's so wrong with that?" he demanded, kissing her again in a way that made it even harder to keep a level and sober head. "Gambling is in my blood, my darling. Have you none in yours? We shall fight like tigers, no doubt, and I can promise to make you miserable every second day of your life. But won't you take a chance on this?"

Still she held back. Her eyes had a look of determined seriousness. She said slowly, "I love to gamble; more than you do, I think. But what happens to us when the game is over and one of us has won or lost? What then?"

He did not speak, but held her away from him, looking down into her flushed face. He seemed to be waiting.

Apparently he was going to offer her no help. Trust him to put her at a disadvantage, she thought, fleetingly. He might, as she well knew, have swept aside her precarious defenses; and in a way she would have welcomed it. He wasn't going to allow her even that luxury. He was leaving her to work the matter out.

She loved him and needed him. She had known this for

some time; and despite his calm look as he waited for her to speak, she was aware that there was a similar urgency in his need for her.

She had no words to say it; not then. Later she might try. She smiled at him and said, "Martha has been urging me to find myself a husband. I really don't think we should disappoint her, do you?"

About the Author

ALTHOUGH SARA HELY WAS BORN IN LONDON, and was a refugee in the United States during the war (World War II), her family is from Ireland, where she lived from the time she was twelve until she got married. Miss Hely now lives in Scotland with her husband, Jan Collins, director of Collins Publishers, and their three children. *The Legend of the Green Man* is Sara Hely's first novel and she is working on another.